The Linda and Gerald Guterman Collection

Auction
Thursday, January 14, 1988 at 10:30 am

Exhibition

Friday, January 8	10 am to 5 pm
Saturday, January 9	10 am to 5 pm
Sunday, January 10	1 pm to 5 pm
Monday, January 11	10 am to 5 pm
Tuesday, January 12	10 am to 5 pm
Wednesday, January 13	10 am to 3 pm

In sending absentee bids this catalogue
may be referred to as 5676 "GUTERMAN"

Cover Illustration: Lot 41

SOTHEBY'S

FOUNDED 1744

1334 York Avenue (at 72nd Street)
New York, NY 10021
Cable: Parkgal, New York
Telex: New York 232643 (SPB UR)
Telephone: (212) 606-7000

Catalogues $35 at the gallery,
$40 by mail, $45 overseas

John L. Marion, Principal Auctioneer
License number 524728

List of post sale price results
will be sent to all catalogue purchasers
4 to 6 weeks after sale

Experts in Charge
George Wachter, 606-7230
Heidi Chin

Absentee Bids
Roberta Louckx, 606-7414
Deborah Hatch

Shipping
Laura Bowman, 606-7511

Purchaser Payments
Edward Upbin, 606-7492

Consignor Payments
John Filipponi, 606-7310

24 Hour Sale Information
Recorded announcements of
current auctions and exhibitions
(212) 606-7245

Expert Departments

American Decorative Arts & Furniture
Leslie B. Keno, 606-7130
William W. Stahl, Jr.

American Folk Art
Nancy Druckman, 606-7225

American Indian, African & Oceanic Art
Dr. Bernard de Grunne, 606-7325
Ellen Napiura *(Consultant)*

American Paintings, Drawings & Sculpture
Peter B. Rathbone, 606-7280
Nan Chisholm
Dara Mitchell
Eda Martin

Antiquities
Richard M. Keresey, 606-7328

Arms & Armour
Florian Eitle, 606-7250
J. David Wille *(Consultant)*

Art Nouveau & Art Deco
Barbara E. Deisroth, 606-7170
Sarah Hill

Books & Manuscripts
David N. Redden, 606-7385
Mary-Jo Kline *(Americana)*
Jane M. O'Connor
Jay Dillon
Selby Kiffer
Marsha Malinowski

Chinese Works of Art
Carol Conover, 606-7332
Mee Seen Loong
Lark E. Mason, Jr.

Chinese Paintings
Arnold Chang, 606-7334

Coins
Mish Tworkowski, 606-7391

Collectibles
Dana Hawkes, 606-7424

Contemporary Paintings, Drawings & Sculpture
Lucy Mitchell-Innes, 606-7254
Leslie Prouty
Anthony Grant

English Furniture
George Read, 606-7577
Alastair A. Stair *(Consultant)*
Larry Sirolli
Peter Rockefeller, 606-7885

European Furniture
Thierry Millerand, 606-7213
Phillips Hathaway
Gillian M. Arthur

European Works of Art & Tapestries
Florian Eitle, 606-7250
J. David Wille *(Consultant)*

Impressionist & Modern Paintings, Drawings & Sculpture
David J. Nash, 606-7360
John L. Tancock
Sharon Schultz
Howard Rutkowski
Marc E. Rosen *(Drawings)*, 606-7154
Laurel Beckett
Barbara Pallenberg *(Regional Fine Arts Director, West Coast),* (213) 274-0340
Helyn Goldenberg *(Regional Fine Arts Director, Midwest/Central),* (312) 642-9001

Islamic Works of Art
Richard M. Keresey, 606-7328

Indian, Himalayan and Southeast Asian Works of Art and Miniatures
Carlton C. Rochell, Jr., 606-7328

Japanese Art
Jane Oliver, 606-7338
Annette Kluss Alvarez

Jewelry
John D. Block, 606-7392
Paul Russo
Jacqueline Fay *(Antique)*
Lisa Hubbard *(West Coast),* (213) 274-0340
Nan Summerfield *(Jewelry West)*
Tracy Sherman *(Canadian Sales)*
Ann Limer Lange *(Arcade)*

Judaica
Jay Weinstein, 606-7387

Latin American Paintings
Anne Horton, 606-7290

Musical Instruments
Charles Rudig, 606-7190

19th Century European Paintings & Drawings
Nancy Harrison, 606-7140
Benjamin F. Doller

19th Century Furniture, Decorations & Works of Art
Elaine Whitmire, 606-7285

Old Master Paintings & Drawings
George Wachter, 606-7230
Heidi Chin
Eunice Williams *(Consultant)*

Paperweights & Glass
Lauren Tarshis, 606-7180

Photographs
Beth Gates-Warren, 606-7240

Porcelain: European & Chinese Export
Letitia Roberts, 606-7180
Debe Cuevas

Pre-Columbian Art
Stacy Goodman, 606-7330
Fatma Turkkan-Wille *(Consultant)*

Prints
Marc E. Rosen, 606-7117
Susan Pinsky
Ruth Ziegler
Tara Reddi
Mary Bartow

Rugs & Carpets
William F. Ruprecht, 606-7380
Mary Jo Otsea

Russian Art, Icons, Objets de Vertu
Gerard Hill, 606-7150

Silver
Kevin L. Tierney, 606-7160
Ian Irving

Vintage Cars
Kirk A. Igler *(Consultant),* 794-0393
Dana Hawkes, 606-7424
Christine Eisenberg *(West Coast),* (213) 274-0340

Watches, Clocks & Scientific Instruments
Daryn Schnipper, 606-7162
Kevin L. Tierney, 606-7160

Sotheby's Arcade Auctions
Sarah S. Negrea *(Silver),* 606-7409
Wiebke Moore *(Decorations),* 606-7409
Jennifer Roth *(Fine Arts),* 606-7516
Amy Parsons *(Fine Arts),* 606-7516
Nan Summerfield *(Jewelry West),* (213) 274-0340
Ann Limer Lange *(Jewelry),* 606-7392
Peter Rockefeller *(Furniture),* 606-7885

Client Service Departments

Appraisals
Deborah Coy Ahearn, 606-7440

Bids
Roberta Louckx, 606-7414

Catalogue Subscriptions
To order catalogues & price lists:
1-800-752-5685
(in New York: 212 628-4604/4616)
For inquiries or difficulties:
David Ganz, 606-7430

Client Accounting
Constance Adamec *(Arcade),* 606-7147
Arlene Kick *(Buyer Accounts),* 606-7491
Gail Skelly *(Seller Accounts),* 606-7310

Client Advisory Services
Eunice S. Carroll, 606-7427
Nancy Forster, 606-7304

Client Financial Services
Timothy M. Trujillo, 606-7484

Corporate Collections
Deborah Coy Ahern, 606-7440

Estates and Trusts
Warren P. Weitman, Jr., 606-7198

Exhibitions
Alfred Bristol, 606-7460

International Office
Elena Echarte Lord, 606-7400

Legal
Marjorie E. Stone, 606-7175

Museum Services
William Woolfenden *(Consultant),* 606-7552

Personnel
Susan Garbrecht, 606-7204

Press Office/Corporate Affairs
Diana Levitt, 606-7176
Matthew Weigman
Jennifer Brown

Restoration: Furniture & Decorations
John Stair, 860-5446

Shipping & Customs Inquiries
Laura Bowman, 606-7511

Sotheby's International Realty
Nancy Loeb, 606-4117

Special Events
Hilary Cushing, 606-7375

Works of Art Program
Stacy Weiss, 606-7822

Sales Conducted by

John L. Marion, John D. Block, David J. Nash, David N. Redden, Marc E. Rosen, William W. Stahl, Jr., Robert C. Woolley, Julian Barran, Nicholas C. Rayner, Julian R. Thompson, Eunice S. Carroll, Gerard J. Hill, Lisa Hubbard, Lucy Mitchell-Innes, George Read, William F. Ruprecht, Richard S. Wolf, Annette Kluss Alvarez, Sarah Shinn Negrea, Department of Consumer Affairs Auctioneers Licensed Numbers (respectively): 524728, 733768, 764786, 736142, 690713, 760961, 678346, 795766, 792131, 815180, 738576, 761969, 794848, 798649, 823084, 794917, 793869, 793375, 822049.

Conditions of Sale

This catalogue, as amended by any posted notices or oral announcements during the sale, is Sotheby's, Inc's and the Consignor's entire agreement with the purchaser relative to the property listed herein. The following Conditions of Sale, the Terms of Guarantee and any glossary contained herein are the complete and only terms and conditions on which all property is offered for sale. The property will be offered by us as agent for the Consignor, unless the catalogue indicates otherwise.

1. The authenticity of the Authorship of property listed in the catalogue is guaranteed as stated in the Terms of Guarantee; except as provided therein, all property is sold "**AS IS**," and neither we nor the Consignor make any warranties or representations of the correctness of the catalogue or other description of the physical condition, size, quality, rarity, importance, medium, provenance, exhibitions, literature or historical relevance of the property and no statement anywhere, whether oral or written, shall be deemed such a warranty or representation. Prospective bidders should inspect the property before bidding to determine its condition, size and whether or not it has been repaired or restored. We and the Consignor make no representations and warranties as to whether the purchaser acquires any copyrights, including but not limited to, any reproduction rights in the property.

2. A premium of 10% of the successful bid price will be added thereto and is payable by the purchaser as part of the total purchase price.

3. We reserve the right to withdraw any property before sale and shall have no liability whatsoever for such withdrawal.

4. Unless otherwise announced by the auctioneer, all bids are per lot as numbered in the catalogue.

5. We reserve the right to reject any bid. The highest bidder acknowledged by the auctioneer will be the purchaser. In the event of any dispute between bidders, or in the event of doubt on our part as to the validity of any bid, the auctioneer will have the final discretion either to determine the successful bidder or to reoffer and resell the article in dispute. If any dispute arises after the sale, our sale record is conclusive. Although in our discretion we will execute order bids or accept telephone bids as a convenience to clients who are not present at auctions, we are not responsible for any errors or omissions in connection therewith.

6. If the auctioneer decides that any opening bid is below the reserve of the article offered, he may reject the same and withdraw the article from sale, and if, having acknowledged an opening bid, he decides that any advance thereafter is insufficient, he may reject the advance.

7. On the fall of the auctioneer's hammer, title to the offered lot will pass to the highest bidder acknowledged by the auctioneer, subject to fulfillment by such bidder of all the conditions set forth herein, and such bidder thereupon (a) assumes full risk and responsibility therefor, and (b) will pay the full purchase price therefor or such part as we may require. In addition to other remedies available to us by law, we reserve the right to impose a late charge of 1½% per month of the total purchase price if payment is not made in accordance with the conditions set forth herein. All property must be removed from our premises by the purchaser at his expense not later than 10 business days following its sale and, if it is not so removed, (i) a handling charge of 1% of the total purchase price per month until its removal will be payable to us by the purchaser, with a minimum of 5% for any property not so removed

within 60 days after the sale, and (ii) we may send the purchased property to a public warehouse for the account, risk and expense of the purchaser. If any applicable conditions herein are not complied with by the purchaser, in addition to other remedies available to us and the Consignor by law, including without limitation the right to hold the purchaser liable for the total purchase price, we at our option may either (a) cancel the sale, retaining as liquidated damages all payments made by the purchaser or (b) resell the property at public auction without reserve, and the purchaser will be liable for any deficiency, costs, including handling charges, the expenses of both sales, our commissions on both sales at our regular rates, all other charges due hereunder and incidental damages. In addition, a defaulting purchaser will be deemed to have granted us a security interest in, and we may retain as collateral security for such purchaser's obligations to us, any property in our possession owned by such purchaser. In the event a purchaser pays a portion of the total purchase price, we may apply such payment, in our sole discretion, to the lot we deem appropriate. We shall have all of the rights accorded a secured party under the New York Uniform Commercial Code with respect to such property and we may apply against such obligations all monies held or received by us for the account of, or due from us to, such purchaser. At our option, payment will not be deemed to have been made in full until we have collected good funds represented by checks, or, in the case of bank or cashier's checks, we have confirmed their authenticity.

8. Lots marked with □ immediately preceding the lot number are offered subject to a reserve, which is the confidential minimum price below which such lot will not be sold. We may implement such reserves by bidding on behalf of the Consignor. In certain instances, the Consignor may pay us less than the standard commission rate where a lot is "bought-in" to protect its reserve. Where the Consignor is indebted to or has a monetary guarantee from us, and in certain other instances, where we or our affiliated companies may have an interest in the offered lots and the proceeds therefrom, other than our commissions, we may bid therefor to protect such interests.

9. Unless exempted by law, the purchaser will be required to pay the combined New York State and local sales tax or any applicable compensating use tax of another state on the total purchase price. The rate of such combined tax is 8¼% in New York City and ranges from 4% to 8¼% elsewhere in New York State.

10. These Conditions of Sale, as well as the purchaser's and our respective rights and obligations hereunder, shall be governed by and the construed and enforced in accordance with the laws of the State of New York. By bidding at an auction, whether present in person or by agent, order bid, telephone or other means, the purchaser shall be deemed to have consented to the exclusive jurisdiction of the state courts of, and the federal courts sitting in, the State of New York.

11. We are not responsible for the acts or omissions in our packing or shipping of purchased lots or other carriers or packers of purchased lots, whether or not recommended by us. Packing and handling of purchased lots is at the entire risk of the purchaser. If the purchaser requests that we obtain an export license for an item containing an endangered species, there will be a charge of $125 for each license obtained.

12. In no event will our liability to a purchaser exceed the purchase price actually paid.

Terms of Guarantee

We guarantee the authenticity of Authorship of each lot contained in this catalogue on the terms and conditions set forth below.

1. Definition of Authorship. "Authorship" means the identity of the creator, the period, culture, source of origin of the property, as the case may be, as set forth in the **Bold Type Heading** of such catalogue entry.

2. Guarantee Coverage. Subject to the exclusions of (i) attributions of paintings, drawings or sculpture executed prior to 1870, and (ii) periods or dates of execution of the property, as explained in Paragraph 5 below, if within five (5) years from the date of the sale of any lot, the original purchaser of record tenders to us a purchased lot in the same condition as when sold through us, and it is established that the identification of Authorship (as defined above) of such lot set forth in the **Bold Type Heading** of this catalogue description of such lot (as amended by any posted notices or oral announcements during the sale) is not substantially correct based on a fair reading of the catalogue including the terms of any Glossary contained herein, the sale of such lot will be rescinded and the original purchase price refunded.

3. Non-Assignability. It is specifically understood that the benefits of this Guarantee are not assignable and shall be applicable only to the original purchaser of the lot from us and not to the subsequent owners or others who have or may acquire an interest therein.

4. Sole Remedy. It is further specifically understood that the remedy set forth herein, namely the rescission of the sale and refund of the original purchase price paid for the lot, is exclusive and in lieu of any other remedy which might otherwise be available as a matter of law.

5. Exclusions. The Guarantee covers only the correctness of description of Authorship (as defined in 1 above) as identified in the **Bold Type Heading** of the catalogue item but does *not* extend to (i) the identity of the creator of paintings, drawings and sculpture executed before 1870 unless these works are determined to be counterfeits, as this is a matter of current scholarly opinion which can change, (ii) the identification of the periods or dates of execution of the property which may be proven inaccurate by means of scientific processes not generally accepted for use until after publication of the catalogue, or (iii) titles or other identification of offered lots or descriptions of physical condition and size, quality, rarity, importance, provenance, medium, exhibitions and literature of historical relevance, which information normally appears in lower case type below the **Bold Type Heading** identifying the Authorship. Although our best judgment is used in attributing paintings, drawings and sculpture created prior to 1870 through the appropriate use of glossary terms, and due care is taken to insure the correctness of the supplemental material which appears below the **Bold Type Heading** of each entry in the catalogue, the Guarantee does not extend to any possible errors or omissions therein.

Guide for prospective buyers

Sotheby's encourages buyers to read through the "Conditions of Sale," "Terms of Guarantee" and "Glossary," if any, which appear on the preceding pages. The following definitions and explanations are provided for the convenience of prospective bidders.

Reserves

Definition:
A "Reserve" is the confidential minimum price agreed between the seller and us, below which the lot will not ordinarily be sold. On unsold lots, less than the full commission may be paid.

Policy:
All lots marked with □ immediately preceding the lot number are being offered subject to a reserve. Our standard advice to sellers is that reserves be set at a percentage of the mean of the estimates, generally somewhat below the low estimate. In no case do we permit a reserve to exceed the high estimate. Estimates for each lot are printed in the catalogue or may be obtained from the expert department.

Implementation:
We bid as agent for the seller to protect reserves. The auctioneer may open the bidding on any lot by placing a bid on behalf of the seller. The auctioneer may further bid on behalf of the seller, up to the amount of the reserve, by placing successive or consecutive bids for a lot, or by placing bids in response to other bidders.

Owned Property

Definition:
"Owned property" is property which, at the time it is offered for sale at auction, is owned solely or partially by us or an affiliate (and in the sale of which we are acting as a principal and not an agent).

Policy:
The purchase of property by us for sale at auction is an insignificant part of our overall business. Direct purchases are only made at the request of a client and, in these cases, only after standard commission sales have been rejected by the client. Reserve prices of property owned by us are set on the same or a lower basis than property sold for other consignors, that is, a reserve will usually be set below the low estimate provided in this catalogue and in no case will it be higher than the high estimate. All property owned by us will be identified in the catalogue as "Property of Sotheby's" or a similar recognizable designation. In some cases, the prior source of property will be identified, e.g., "Property from the Estate of John Doe sold by order of the present owner, Sotheby's."

Implementation:
Bidding by us to protect reserves on property is effected in the same way as bidding to protect reserves on property consigned by an outside seller.

Buyer's Premium

A premium of 10% will be added to the successful bid price of all property sold by us, whether consigned to us or "owned property" as defined above, and whether picked up or delivered, and this premium is payable by all purchasers without exception.

Exportation Permits

Certain property sold at auction by us may be subject to the provisions of the Endangered Species Act of 1973, the Marine Mammal Protection Act of 1972, the Migratory Bird Act of 1982 and the N.Y. State Environmental Conservation Law. In order to export these items, special licenses must be obtained from the Department of the Interior, United States Fish and Wildlife Service. Some items may not be exported (such as items containing whale bone), and others may not be resold once purchased. As a courtesy, Sotheby's is willing to attempt to obtain such licenses on behalf of the purchaser for a fee of $125 per license. However, there are no assurances that any such license can be obtained. Please contact the appropriate expert department if you have any questions.

Sales Tax

New York State sales tax is charged on any purchases picked up or delivered in New York State, unless the purchaser (regardless of state or country of business) has given Sotheby's a valid exemption issued by New York State. Purchases shipped to California, Florida, Illinois, Massachusetts, New Jersey, Pennsylvania, Texas, and Washington, D.C. are subject to the sales tax of those states. If you have any questions regarding your sales tax liability, or need assistance in obtaining a New York exemption, please contact our Customer Billing Department at (212) 606-7464 before placing your bids.

Estimates

Sotheby's catalogues provide detailed descriptions and auction estimates for each lot included in a sale. These estimates are guides for prospective bidders and should not be relied upon as representations or predictions of actual selling prices. Estimates are determined well in advance of the sale date and are subject to revision. Please contact the expert in charge of the sale if you have any questions.

Expert Advice

Sotheby's experts and Client Service representatives are available at our pre-sale exhibitions, and by appointment, to advise prospective bidders on particular objects or on any aspect of the auction process.

Currency Conversion Board

For our clients' convenience, a computerized display board, which converts U.S. dollars into a variety of foreign currencies, is operated during some sales. Foreign currency amounts displayed on this board are approximations. While every effort is made to use the latest exchange rate information available, the conversion display is for convenient reference only and is not to be relied upon as a precise invoice amount. We assume no responsibility for any errors or omissions in foreign or U.S. currency amounts shown. The total purchase price and applicable taxes are payable in U.S. dollars only.

Bidding

Bidding at all auctions is by paddle. Please register for your paddle at the entrance to the salesroom. If your bid is successful at the auction, your paddle number will be called out by the auctioneer, or you will be asked to sign a bid confirmation card upon the fall of the hammer. Unless you have previously established credit or made payment arrangements, you will not be permitted to take delivery of your purchases until after your check has cleared. To avoid such delays, you may apply for a Check Acceptance Account before attending your first auction by filling out an application available from our cashier.

Absentee Bids

If you are unable to attend an auction, you may use the "Absentee Bid Form" provided at the back of this catalogue. Following your instructions, Sotheby's will act on your behalf to try to purchase the lot or lots of your choice for the lowest price possible – and never for more than the top amount you indicate. Absentee bidding, a free service handled in strictest confidence by our Bid Department, allows you to participate in any Sotheby's auction worldwide. For more detailed information, see "Guide to Absentee Bidders" at the back of this catalogue or call Roberta Louckx at (212) 606-7414.

Removal of Property

Unless other arrangements have been agreed upon, we must ask buyers to remove their purchases by 5 pm on the tenth business day following the sale. Purchases not removed within this time will be subject to a handling charge, as outlined in paragraph 7 of the "Conditions of Sale." The packing and handling of purchased lots by our employees is undertaken solely as a courtesy to our clients, and in the case of fragile articles, will be undertaken only at our discretion. In no event will we be liable for damage to glass or frames, regardless of the cause.

The packing and handling of purchased lots by our employees is undertaken solely as a courtesy to our clients, and in the case of fragile articles, will be undertaken only at our discretion. In no event will we be liable for damage to glass or frames, regardless of the cause.

Although we recommend the use of professional packers, books and small articles which are not fragile can be packed on our premises for a nominal charge, and, at our sole discretion, be sent by mail or other carrier. Prints and drawings in glazed frames cannot be handled in this manner.

Sotheby's Art Transport Department and the staff at any of our regional offices can make all the arrangements necessary for shipping purchases to you. There is no charge for this service, but actual shipping expenses and packing and insurance charges are payable by the client. For further information please call Laura Bowman at (212) 606-7511.

Guide for prospective sellers

If you have property you wish to sell at auction, please call the appropriate expert department to arrange for a consultation. (A list of expert departments appears in the front of this catalogue.) If you are unsure which department would handle your property, or if you have a variety of objects to sell, please call one of our general representatives. Please be advised that no property will be offered for sale absent receipt by us of a signed consignment agreement:

Fine Arts Representatives
Beverly Miller, (212) 606-7120

Decorative Arts Representative
(212) 606-7409

Inspection of Property

You may bring your property – or photographs if it is not portable – directly to our galleries where our experts will give you auction estimates and advice. There is no charge for this service, but we request that you telephone ahead for an appointment. Inspection hours are 9:30 am to 5 pm, Monday through Friday.

Our experts will provide a free preliminary auction estimate subject to a final auction estimate after first-hand inspection, if you send a clear photograph of each item, or a representative group of photographs if you have a large collection. Please be sure to include the dimensions, artist's signature or maker's mark, medium, physical condition, and any other relevant information.

Evaluations of property can also be made at your home. The usual fees for such visits outside of Manhattan are: other New York City boroughs/$100 per half-day; elsewhere in North America/$250 per day. (Travel expenses are additional.) These fees may be rebated if you consign your property for sale at Sotheby's within one year of the date of the visit.

Experts from our Beverly Hills office are available for inspection visits in the western United States. For more information, please call (213) 274-0340.

Standard Commission Rates

Sellers are charged 10% of the successful bid price for each lot sold for $5,000 or more. A commission of 15% is charged for each lot sold for $1,000 or more but less than $5,000, and 20% for each lot sold for less than $1,000. There is a minimum handling charge of $100 for any lot sold. If your property fails to reach the reserve price and remains unsold, you pay a reduced commission rate of 5% of the reserve figure. The minimum handling charge for any object that does not sell is $75. (For more information about reserves, please refer to "Reserves" in "Guide to Prospective Buyers.")

Shipping Arrangements

Sotheby's Art Transport Department and the staff at any of our regional offices can advise you on the easiest and safest way to have your property delivered to our galleries. This service is free, but actual packing, shipping and insurance charges are payable by our clients. (While we may recommend packers and shippers, we are not responsible for their acts or omissions.) For further information please call Laura Bowman at (212) 606-7511.

Appraisals

Sotheby's Appraisal Company can prepare appraisals for insurance, estate tax, charitable contributions, family division or other purposes.

Appraisal fees vary according to the nature and amount of work to be undertaken but will always be highly competitive. Flat rates can be quoted based on expert time required, value and processing costs. Travel expenses are additional.

We shall be pleased to refund the appraisal fee pro rata if the appraised property is consigned to us for sale within one year after the appraisal is completed. For further information please call (212) 606-7440.

Financial Services

Sotheby's offers advances on consignments and makes loans secured by collections which are not intended for sale.

For further information regarding qualifications and terms, please call Mitchell Zuckerman at (212) 606-3008.

Sotheby's catalogues, price lists and Newsletter

Illustrated catalogues, prepared by Sotheby's experts, are published for all regularly scheduled auctions and may be purchased singly or by annual subscription. (Catalogue subscribers automatically receive *Sotheby's Newsletter* at no additional charge.)

Printed lists of the prices realized at each auction are available at our galleries approximately three weeks following the auction, and are sent directly to catalogue purchasers and subscribers.

Sotheby's Newsletter, published nine times a year, provides an advance calendar of all Sotheby's sales worldwide and full-color photographs of auction highlights. A complimentary copy is available upon request. Annual subscriptions are $15 ($20 overseas).

For more information, or to subscribe to our catalogues or *Newsletter*, ask for our brochure. Write or call Sotheby's Subscription Department, P.O. Box 5290, FDR Station, New York, N.Y. 10150-5290. Telephone: 1-800-752-5686. (In New York: 212-628-4604/4616)

Glossary for Paintings

The following are examples of the terminology used in this catalogue. Please note that all statements in this catalogue as to authorship, period, culture, source or origin are qualified statements and are made subject to the provisions of the Conditions of Sale and the Terms of Guarantee printed in this catalogue.

*Giovanni Bellini
Followed, under the heading "Authorship," by the words "ascribed to the named artist."
In our opinion, *a work by the artist* (when the artist's forename is not known, a series of asterisks followed by the surname of the artist, whether preceded by an initial or not, indicates that, in our opinion, the work is by the artist named). While this is our highest category of authenticity, no unqualified statement as to authorship is made or intended.

Attributed to Giovanni Bellini
In our opinion, *probably* a work by the artist but less certainty as to authorship is expressed than in the preceding category.

Studio of Giovanni Bellini
In our opinion, a work by *an unknown hand in the studio* of the artist which may or may not have been executed under the artist's direction.

Circle of Giovanni Bellini
In our opinion, a work by an *as yet unidentified but distinct hand* closely associated with the named artist but not necessarily his pupil.

Style of . . . Follower of Giovanni Bellini
In our opinion, a work by a painter working *in the artist's style*, contemporary or nearly contemporary, but not necessarily his pupil.

Manner of Giovanni Bellini
In our opinion, a work in the style of the artist *and of a later date*.

After Giovanni Bellini
In our opinion, *a copy* of a known work of the artist.

The term *signed* and/or *dated* and/or *inscribed* means that, in our opinion, a signature and/or date and/or inscription are from the hand of the artist.

The term *bears* a signature and/or a date and/or an inscription means that, in our opinion, a signature and/or date and/or inscription have been added by another hand.

Dimensions are given height before width.

Pictures are framed unless otherwise stated.

Index of Artists

The Linda and Gerald Guterman Collection

THURSDAY, JANUARY 14, 1988 AT 10:30 AM

(lots 1 to 47)

*Jan Asselijn (*ca.* 1610–1652)

☐ 1   A MEDITERRANEAN COASTAL VIEW WITH SHIPPING
AND MARINERS BY A FORT

signed in monogram lower right
oil on canvas
39 by 33¾ in.   99 by 86 cm.

Provenance:
Lord Braybrooke, Audley End, Essex, thence by descent to
The Hon. R. C. H. Neville (Sale: Christie's, London, December 11, 1984, lot
123, illus.)

Literature:
Richard, 3rd Baron Braybrooke, *The History of Audley End*, 1836, p. 119, no. 11
R. J. B. Walker, *Audley End Catalogue*, 1964, p. 14, no. 10

$60,000–80,000

1

*Hendrick Avercamp (1585–1634)

☐ 2   WINTER SCENE WITH SKATERS ON A FROZEN RIVER,
A VILLAGE BEYOND

signed in monogram middle right and dated *1609*
oil on panel
11½ by 17 in.   29 by 44.5 cm.

Provenance:
Paul Delaroff, St. Petersburg (Sale: Paris, April 23, 1914, no. 15, sold for 500 francs)
Baron H. Thyssen-Bornemisza, Schloss Rohoncz, 1930
Mme. la Baronne Gabriele Bentinck, Paris, 1956
Bier, Haarlem, 1962
Sale: Sotheby's, London, July 10, 1974, lot 120, illus. (as "The Property of an Estate bequeathed to the Weizmann Institute of Science")

Exhibited:
Munich, Neue Pinakothek, *Exhibition of the Schloss Rohoncz Collection*, 1930, no. 10
New York, Minskoff Cultural Center (to benefit the Appeal of Conscience Foundation), *The Golden Ambience: Dutch Landscape Painting in the Seventeenth Century*, 1985, (Catalogue by Walter Liedtke), cat. no. 4, illus.

Literature:
Clara J. Welcker, *Hendrick Avercamp, 1585–1634; Barent Avercamp, 1612–1679: Schilders tot Campen*, 1933, p. 203, no. 4, illus. plate VIII, fig. XXI
Clara J. Welcker, *Hendrick Avercamp, 1585–1634; Barent Avercamp, 1612–1679: Schilders tot Campen*, 1979, p. 203, no. 4, illus. plate VIII, fig. XXI

$300,000–400,000

2

*Gerrit Adriaensz. Berckheyde (1638–1698)

☐ 3   THE COURTYARD OF THE BINNENHOF, THE HAGUE

signed lower left
oil on canvas
21 by 24¼ in.   53.5 by 61.5 cm.

This painting will be included in the forthcoming monograph on Berckheyde by Prof. Cynthia Lawrence as an autograph work in a note discussing Berckheyde's depiction of the Binnenhof.

The Binnenhof (or inner court), in the center of The Hague, is where Count Willem II built a castle in the 13th century. The town that grew around it became known as *'s Gravenhage* (Count's Hedge), the city's formal name. It is today the center for local government offices, as well as the home of The Netherlands' two-chamber parliament. Although most of the original 13th century structure has now been significantly altered, much of the 17th century architectural work in and around the Binnenhof remains.

Provenance:
Sale: Christie's, London, February 20, 1986, lot 158, illus.
Johnny van Haeften, Ltd., London

$140,000–180,000

*Adriaen Brouwer (1605/6–1638)

☐ 4   PEASANTS IN A TAVERN INTERIOR

oil on panel
8½ by 7¾ in.   21 by 19.5 cm.

C. Hofstede de Groot, in *A Catalogue Raisonné of the Works of the Most Eminent Dutch Painters of the Seventeenth Century*, 1910, vol. III, p. 578, no. 49e, records a painting which may be identifiable with the present picture and has the following provenance: La Bouexiere (Sale: Steyaert, Paris, March 14, 1843, no. 5), and literature: Jean-Baptiste Descamps, *La Vie des peintres flamands, allemands et hollandois*, 1753–64, vol. II, p. 139.

Provenance:
Sale: Sotheby's, New York, January 20, 1983, lot 106, illus.

$40,000–60,000

4

*Pieter Brueghel, the Younger (*ca.* 1564–1637/38)

☐ 5   THE ADORATION OF THE MAGI

oil on panel
16 by 22½ in.   40.5 by 57 cm.

Provenance:
The Lord Trevor (Sale: Christie's, London, July 9, 1982, lot 89, illus.)

Exhibited:
London, Royal Academy, *Flemish and Belgian Art 1300–1900*, 1927, no. 233

Literature:
Georges Marlier, *Pierre Brueghel Le Jeune*, 1969, p. 85, no. 21
$300,000–400,000

*Pieter Claesz. (1597/98–1661)

☐ 6   STILL LIFE WITH GLASS WARE AND A GILT CUP

signed in monogram middle right and dated *1640*
oval, oil on panel
22 by 16¼ in.   56 by 41 cm.

This painting is accompanied by a certificate from Prof. Ingvar Bergstrom dated June 14, 1982, Goteborg. In it, he discusses at length both the iconographic meaning of the objects portrayed and the significance of this unusual and striking composition.

The *vanitas* intent is evident in the well-known symbol of the overturned glass, and Bergstrom cites the inscription (translated from Dutch) from another Claesz. still-life with a similar glass:

> *The glass is empty, Time is ended*
> *The candle has burnt itself out, Man is dumb*

Nuts, as seen at the left side of the painting, were commonly understood in the seventeenth century to symbolize sinfulness and worldliness (see C. G. Stridbeck, *Bruegelstudien . . .*, 1956, pp. 349–350, and footnote 19), while the covered cup, so prominent in the composition, may be seen as the triumph of Christian virtue over earthly concerns. This is indicated by the figure with spear and shield and eyes turned "heavenward," extremely similar to the *Miles Christianus* soldier (see A. Wang, *Miles Christianus im 16. und 17. Jahrhundert und seine mittelalterliche Tradition*, 1975, figs. 1–4, 7) and the *Dispregio del monde* of Cesare Ripa's *Iconologia*, 1603, pp. 107–8.

The focus of this composition on a single object makes it likely that the cup portrayed did once exist, although its whereabouts are no longer known. There is also a Claesz. work of similar composition (signed and dated *1641*) showing a similar tall, covered vessel which is now in the Frans Halsmuseum, Haarlem. That cup was made by the silversmiths Jacob P. van Alckemade and Ernst J. van Vianen on a commission from the Brewer's or St. Martin's Guild of that city in 1604/5; it bears the year letter for 1604/5 and is based on designs by Hendrik de Keyser and drawings by Hendrik Goltzius.

Provenance:
Johnny van Haeften, Ltd., London

$80,000–120,000

*Adriaen Coorte (active by 1685–1723)

□ 7   STILL LIFE OF A BOWL OF STRAWBERRIES AND A BUNCH OF ASPARAGUS
WITH CURRANTS AND GOOSEBERRIES

signed lower right and dated *1703*
oil on canvas
14¼ by 16½ in.   36 by 42 cm.

A similar arrangement of asparagus and a bowl of strawberries is part of a
larger still life by Coorte, also signed and dated *1703*, in the Koninklijk Museum
voor Schone Kunsten, Antwerp, and a painting by Coorte of a similar bunch
of asparagus, signed and dated *1703*, is in the Fitzwilliam Museum, Cambridge
(see Laurens J. Bol, *Adriaen Coorte*, 1977, nos. 53a and 54, figs. 29 and 30).

Provenance:
Sale: Sotheby's, Monaco, June 22, 1985, lot 46, illus.
David Koetser, Zurich

$400,000–600,000

*Aelbert Cuyp (1620–1691)

☐ 8   THE CONVERSION OF SAINT PAUL

signed lower right
oil on panel
28 by 35¾ in.   71 by 91 cm.

As Susan Donahue Kuretsky points out in her entry on this painting for the 1980/81 *Gods, Saints and Heroes* exhibition (see below), history paintings by Aelbert Cuyp are rare. Several depictions of St. Paul by Cuyp's uncle, Benjamin Gerritsz. Cuyp, are known, but the present composition differs markedly from those interpretations. In this painting, great emphasis is given to the horses in the scene, which is consistent with Aelbert's interest in equestrian and hunting themes. Furthermore, the golden lighting and Mediterranean architecture indicate the influence of the Dutch Italianate landscape painters, such as Jan Both.

Provenance:
Possibly an Amsterdam sale, January 24, 1763
Possibly J. van der Linden van Slingelandt (Sale: 1785, no. 101)
Possibly Blanken (Sale: The Hague, June 4, 1800)
Captain James Aston Robert-West, Alscot Park, Warwickshire, 1950–64
Sale: Christie's, London, June 26, 1964, no. 122
Dr. H. Wetzlar, Amsterdam, 1964 (Sale: Sotheby Mak van Waay, Amsterdam June 9, 1977, no. 66)
J. H. van Litsenburg, Amsterdam
Charles Roelofsz, Amsterdam

Exhibited:
Laren, Singer Museum, *The Art of Collecting*, 1966, no. 18, pl. 22
Dordrecht, Dordrechts Museum, *Aelbert Cuyp en zyn familie*, 1978, cat. no. 27
Washington, D.C., National Gallery of Art, *Gods, Saints, and Heroes*, November 2, 1980–January 4, 1981; Detroit, Institute of Arts, February 16–April 19, 1981; Amsterdam, Rijksmuseum, May 18–July 19, 1981, p. 272, no. 80 (catalogue entry by Susan Donahue Kuretsky)

Literature:
John Smith, *A Catalogue Raisonné of the Works of the Most Eminent Dutch, Flemish, and French Painters*, 1834, vol. V, p. 296, note to no. 35
C. Hofstede de Groot, *Catalogue Raisonné of the Works of the Most Eminent Dutch Painters of the Seventeenth Century*, 1909, vol. II, no. 9A (?) and 10 ("a rich composition, finely painted, full of fire and striking effect. Probably by Benjamin Cuyp.")
S. Reiss, *Aelbert Cuyp*, 1975, p. 204

$80,000–120,000

*Jacob Gerritsz. Cuyp (1594–1651/52)

□ 9   PORTRAIT OF MARIA STRICKE VAN SCHARLAKEN

signed lower left and dated *1650*, inscribed right center with the age of the sitter *AEtatis 3.3 MA*
oil on panel
32 by 24½ in.   81.3 by 62 cm.

An old inscription on the reverse of the present picture reads "Marie Strick van Scharlaaken Regneer's Dogter. Geboren den 13ten October 1646, en overleden den 15ten June 1669."

Maria Stricke van Scharlaken (1646–69) was the daughter of Reynier Stricke, a merchant from Holstein who came to Amsterdam and married Alida van Scharlaken of Dordrecht, a daughter from one of the oldest patrician families in The Netherlands. Their children combined the parents' names due to the social standing of the van Scharlaken family. Maria married Pieter Brandwijk von Blockland, a Burgomaster of Dordrecht, who was related to the Beelaerts van Blokland family.

Provenance:
James Tulloch, London, 1857
Dr. F. Schoni, Zurich, 1957
Spink and Co., London, 1975
Sale: Christie's, New York, May 9, 1985, lot 7 (as Aelbert Cuyp)

Exhibited:
Oklahoma City, Oklahoma Museum of Art, *Masters of the Portrait*, 1978, no. 6 (as Aelbert Cuyp)
Fort Worth, Texas, Kimbell Art Museum, *Old Master Paintings: Cranach to Corot*, 1982, no. 3, illustrated (as Aelbert Cuyp)

Literature:
Gustav Waagen, *Galleries and Cabinets of Art in Great Britain*, 1857, p. 200 (as Aelbert Cuyp)
C. Hofstede de Groot, *A Catalogue Raisonné of the Works of the Most Eminent Dutch Painters of the Seventeenth Century*, 1909, vol. II, p. 34, no. 96 (as Aelbert Cuyp)
Allison McNeil Kettering, *The Dutch Arcadia*, 1983, pp. 9, 69, 176, no. 1650 and fig. 67 (as Aelbert Cuyp)
Richard Dorment, *British Paintings in the Philadelphia Museum of Art from the Seventeenth through the Nineteenth Century*, 1986, p. 310, under no. 86, illus. fig. 86-1 (as Aelbert Cuyp)

$150,000–200,000

*Jacob Duck (1600–1660)

☐ 10   GUARDROOM INTERIOR WITH SLEEPING SOLDIERS AND
ELEGANT FIGURES BEYOND

signed lower center
oil on panel
16½ by 25 in.   42 by 63.5 cm.

Provenance:
Sir Charles Clore (Sale: Philips, London, December 10, 1985, lot 42, illus.)
Bob P. Haboldt, New York

$70,000–90,000

*Karel Dujardin (1621/22(?)–1678)

☐ 11   CROSSING THE FORD

signed lower left
oil on canvas
20 by 18¼ in.   *50.7 by 46.5 cm.*

While in the collection of the Prince de Condé (see provenance below), this painting was engraved by La Bas with the title *La Belle après dinée* (see *Mercure de France*, December 1781, p. 44).

Provenance:
Louis Joseph de Bourbon, Prince de Condé
M. de Sereville (Sale: Paris, January 22, 1811, pp. 16–17, lot 28)
Comte de Perregaux (Sale: Paris, December 8, 1841, pp. 36–38, lot 16)
Baron James de Rothschild, Paris
Didier Aaron, New York

Exhibited:
New York, Richard L. Feigen & Co., *Landscape Painting in Rome, 1595–1675*, January 30–March 23, 1985 (catalogue by Ann Sutherland Harris), p. 183, cat. no. 29, illus. (as datable near the end of the 1650's, lent by Mr. and Mrs. Guterman)

Literature:
John Smith, *Catalogue Raisonné of the Works of the Most Eminent Dutch, Flemish, and French Painters*, 1834, vol. V, pp. 254–55, no. 66
John Smith, *Supplement to the Catalogue Raisonné of the Works of the Most Eminent Dutch, Flemish, and French Painters*, 1842, p. 642, no. 14
C. Hofstede de Groot, *Beschreibendes und kritisches Verzeichnis der Werke der hervorragendsten Hollandischen Maler des XVII Jahrhunderts*, 1926, vol. IX, pp. 355–56, no. 227
E. Brochhagen, *Karel Dujardin*, Inaugural-Dissertation, University of Koln, 1958, p. 48, no. 191

$150,000–200,000

11

*Karel Dujardin (1621/22(?)–1678)

□ 12   EXTENSIVE RIVER LANDSCAPE WITH A HERD OF SHEEP
         AND RESTING SHEPHERDS ON A HILL

oil on panel
35½ by 45¼ in.   90.5 by 115 cm.

Formerly ascribed to Jan Asselijn, the present picture has been properly
identified as the work of Karel Dujardin by Otto Naumann, Renate Ternek,
Dr. Anne Charlotte Steland and Dr. Albert Blankert. In a photo-certificate
dated July 4, 1984, Dr. Blankert suggests a date of 1675–78 for this picture,
while Dr. Steland proposes an earlier date of *circa* 1655. Ann Sutherland Harris
(see below) considers this painting to be a late work, *circa* 1675, executed
while the artist was in Italy.

Provenance:
Christophe Janet, New York

Exhibited:
New York, Richard L. Feigen & Co., *Landscape Painting in Rome, 1595–1675,*
January 30–March 23, 1985 (catalogue by Ann Sutherland Harris), p. 178,
cat. no. 28, illus. (lent by Mr. and Mrs. Guterman)
New York, Minskoff Cultural Center (to benefit the Appeal of Conscience
Foundation), *The Golden Ambience: Dutch Landscape Painting in the Seventeenth
Century,* 1985, (catalogue by Walter Liedtke), cat. no. 21, illus.

$80,000–120,000

12

Attributed to Gerbrand van den Eeckhout (1621–1674)

☐ 13   THE ADORATION OF THE MAGI

oil on canvas
48½ by 41¼ in.   123 by 105 in.

There is a version of this composition, very similar in size, in the collection of Queen Elizabeth II. That work was acquired from Sir Francis Baring in 1814. The present painting also has Baring provenance: in the 1937 sale (see below), Sir Thomas Baring is cited as owner from 1845–48. The earlier histories of these two works have been often confused, and the pre-1814 provenance as listed here was first suggested in the 1986 sale (see below), based largely on the present painting being the only known version on canvas. Both pictures were long considered to be the work of Rembrandt, the present painting until at least 1937.

The attribution to Gerbrand van den Eeckhout of the Royal Collection painting was first suggested by K. Bauch, *Rembrandt Gemälde*, 1965, p. 6, no. 88. While C. White (see literature below) finds this ascription plausible, W. Sumowski, in *Gemälde der Rembrandt-Schüler*, 1983, Vol. II, p. 738, no. 454, states the Royal collection picture to be by a follower of Eeckhout.

Provenance:
probably Jacques Meyers (Sale: Rotterdam, September 9, 1722, lot 168, sold for 180 florins)
probably William Six (Sale: Amsterdam, May 12, 1734, lot 58, sold for 250 florins, purchased by S. Ligtenhorst)
probably M. Servad (Sale: Amsterdam, June 25, 1778, lot 80, described as dated 1657, sold for 1,000 florins, purchased by Fouquet)
possibly The Gallery, 22 Piccadilly, London, 1809, no. 34
Sir Thomas Baring, Bt., Stratton (Sale: Christie's, London, June 2–3, 1848, lot 113, sold for 135 guineas, purchased by Nieuwenhuys)
Thomas Baring, son of the above, 1854
The Earl of Northbrook, by 1889, by descent to
The Right Honorable Florence Anita, Countess of Northbrook, C.B.E. (Sale: Christie's, London, June 11, 1937 (stencil on the reverse), lot 16, as Rembrandt, sold for 100 guineas, purchased by Spink)
A. J. Grotendorst, Nijmegen, 1963
Sale: Christie's, London, April 11, 1986, lot 39, illus. (as by Eeckhout)

Exhibited:
London, British Institution, 1845, no. 2 (as Rembrandt, lent by Sir Thomas Baring)

Literature:
probably John Smith, *Catalogue Raisonné of the Works of the Most Eminent Dutch, Flemish and French Painters*, 1836, vol. VII, pp. 25–26, no. 62 (as dated 1657, from the catalogue of the 1778 Servad sale, and as by Rembrandt van Rijn)
Dr. Waagen, *Art Treasures in Great Britain*, 1854, vol. II, p. 182 (as by Rembrandt)
A Descriptive Catalogue of the Collection of Pictures belonging to the Earl of Northbrook, 1889, p. 61, no. 84 (as by Rembrandt)
C. Hofstede de Groot, *Catalogue Raisonné of the Works of the Most Eminent Dutch Painters of the Seventeenth Century*, 1916, vol. VI, pp. 70–71, under no. 84 (confused with the Buckingham Palace picture)
C. White, *The Dutch Pictures in the Collection of Her Majesty the Queen*, 1982, p. 109

$60,000–80,000

*Barent Fabritius (1624–1673)

☐ 14   SHEPHERD WITH A FLUTE AND A RING, POSSIBLY A SELF-PORTRAIT

signed middle right and dated *1660*
oil on canvas
28½ by 25 cm.   72.5 by 63 cm.

Pont (see literature below) suggests that this picture is a self-portrait and
that it once had a pendant, a likely conclusion based on the shepherd's gesture
which seems directed towards another figure, probably a shepherdess. Sumowski (see 1983 literature below) concurs with the suggestion that the present
painting probably had a pendant. He further notes the influence of Carel
Fabritius evident in the placement of the figure against the sky and clouds
similar to Carel's *Self-Portrait* of 1654 in the National Gallery, London.

Provenance:
Capt. E. C. Palmer, Woodburn Green, Bucks, circa 1958
George Adams (Sale: William Doyle Galleries, New York, September 19, 1979,
lot 157, as *Self-Portrait*)

Exhibited:
Manila, Metropolitan Museum of Manila, *Inaugural Exhibition*, 1976–77
Vaduz, Liechtenstein, *Masterpieces of Dutch Art from the Golden Age*, 1978
Amsterdam, Waterman Gallery, *The Impact of a Genius: Rembrandt, his Pupils
and Followers in the Seventeenth Century*, 1983, p. 142, no. 26, illus. p. 143, catalogue
by Albert Blankert, Ben Broos, Ernst van de Watering, Guido Jansen, and
Willem van de Watering (lent by Mr. and Mrs. Guterman)

Literature:
D. Pont, *Barent Fabritius: 1624–1673*, 1958, p. 159, addendum 8, illus.
Werner Sumowski, Review of Pont, *B. Fabritius, Kunstchronik*, no. 12, 1959, pp.
289, 293, 294
Gotz Eckardt, *Selbstbildnisse Niederländischer Maler des 17 Jahrhunderts*, 1971, p. 183
J. G. van Gelder, "Frühe Rembrandt-Sammlungen," in O. von Simpson and
J. Kelch, *Neue Beiträge Rembrandt-Forschung*, 1973, p. 192, illus. pl. 38, fig. 157
A. McNeill Kettering, *Arcadia, Pastoral Themes in Seventeenth Century Dutch Art*,
1974, vol. I, p. 524, illus. fig. 144
Walter Liedtke, "The Three 'Parables' by Barent Fabritius, with a chronologi-
cal list of his paintings dating from about 1660 onward," *Burlington Magazine*,
March, 1977, pp. 325–426
V. Herms Draht, "Kunsthandel . . . (Auktionen USA)," *Pantheon*, 1980, no.
38, p. 87, illus.
Werner Sumowski, *Drawings of the Rembrandt School*, 1981, vol. IV, p. 1788
Christopher Brown, *Fabritius*, 1981, p. 50, illus. fig. 43
Werner Sumowski, *Gemälde der Rembrandt-Schüler*, 1983, vol. II, p. 923, no. 587,
illus. p. 963

$100,000–150,000

14

$341,000

Govaert Flinck (1615–1660)

☐ 15   PORTRAIT OF A RABBI

oil on panel
24½ by 20½ in.   62 by 52 cm.

This picture was long attributed to Rembrandt by a number of scholars; Jacob Rosenberg first published it as a work by Govaert Flinck in 1948. Other scholars have since confirmed the attribution to Flinck, and it has most recently been published as Flinck by Werner Sumowski, following the 1981 sale. Von Moltke suggests that the picture described by Waagen (Supplement, p. 290) may be identifiable with the present picture. If so the provenance should include: Joseph Sandars, Taplow House, near Maidenhead, before 1857. Von Moltke dates this painting *circa* 1640–42.

Provenance:
possibly Philip Miles, Bristol, about 1816, thence by descent to
Sir Philip Miles, Bart., Leigh Court, 1884
Prince Demidoff, Palazzo San Donato, Florence, 1885
Charles T. Yerkes, New York (Sale: American Art Association, New York, April 7, 1910, lot 114, cat. no. 82, illus., as by Rembrandt van Rijn)
Ambrose Monell, New Haven, Connecticut and New York (Sale: American Art Association, November 28, 1930, no. 59, as by Rembrandt van Rijn)
Oscar B. Cintas, New York (Sale: Parke-Bernet Galleries, New York, May 1, 1963, lot 14, as by Rembrandt van Rijn)
Sale: Sotheby Parke Bernet, New York, January 8, 1981, lot 119, illus. (as by Govaert Flinck)

Exhibited:
Detroit, Michigan, Detroit Institute of Arts, *Paintings by Rembrandt*, 1930, no. 10, illus. (as by Rembrandt van Rijn)
New York, World's Fair, 1940, *Masterpieces of Art*, no. 88A, illus. (as by Rembrandt van Rijn)
New York, Brooklyn Museum, 1963
Amsterdam, Waterman Gallery, *The Impact of a Genius: Rembrandt, his Pupils and Followers in the Seventeenth Century*, 1983, p. 160, no. 35, illus. p. 161, catalogue by Albert Blankert, Ben Broos, Ernst van de Watering, Guido Jansen, and Willem van de Watering (loaned by Mr. Guterman)

Literature:
W. von Bode, *Complete Work of Rembrandt*, 1899, vol. III, no. 202 (as by Rembrandt)
Adolphe Rosenberg, *The Work of Rembrandt*, p. 189
Eugene Dutuit, *Catalogue Historique et Descriptif des Tableaux et Dessins de Rembrandt*, 1885, p. 47
Adolphe Rosenberg and W. R. Valentiner, *Rembrandt (Klassiker der Kunst)*, 1908, p. 187 (as by Rembrandt)
C. Hofstede de Groot, *Catalogue Raisonné of the Works of the Most Eminent Dutch Painters of the Seventeenth Century*, 1916, vol. VI, no. 409 (as Rembrandt)
Adolphe Rosenberg and W. R. Valentiner, *The Work of Rembrandt*, 1921, p. 189
W. R. Valentiner, *Rembrandt Paintings in America*, 1932, no. 57 (as by Rembrandt)
Jacob Rosenberg, *Rembrandt (Concordance of Paintings)*, 1948, p. 243 (as probably by Govaert Flinck)
A. Bredius, *The Paintings of Rembrandt* (Phaidon Edition), n.d., p. 12, no. 209 (notes that the attribution to Rembrandt is doubted by some authorities)
J. W. Von Moltke, *Govaert Flinck*, 1965, p. 102, no. 178, illus. p. 103 (as by Govaert Flinck)
K. Bauch, *Rembrandt Gemälde*, 1966, p. 47 (as Manner of Salomon Koninck)
A. Bredius, revised by H. Gerson, *Rembrandt*, 1969, p. 565, no. 209 (as by Govaert Flinck)
Werner Sumowski, *Gemälde der Rembrandt-Schuler*, vol. II, 1983, p. 1035, no. 678, illus. p. 1110 (as Govaert Flinck)

$150,000–200,000

15

*Jan van Goyen (1596–1656)

□ 16   EXTENSIVE BEACH SCENE, POSSIBLY AT SCHEVENINGEN, WITH FIGURES AND
        HORSE DRAWN CARTS NEAR A VILLAGE AND SAILBOATS IN THE DISTANCE

signed lower right and dated *1634*
oil on panel
20½ by 32½ in.   52 by 82.5 cm.

Provenance:
The Earl of Elgin, Broomhall, Dunfermline (Sale: Christie's, November 27,
1959, no. 23, illus., purchased by Thos. Agnew & Sons for 5,250 guineas)
Mr. and Mrs. E. A. Leavitt-Shamley, The Holt, Upham
Mr. and Mrs. J. Seward Johnson (Sale: Sotheby Parke Bernet, New York,
January 8, 1981, lot 8, illus., and illus. on cover)
French & Co., Inc., New York

Exhibited:
Edinburgh, Royal Institution, 1819, no. 35
New York, Minskoff Cultural Center (to benefit the Appeal of Conscience
Foundation), *The Golden Ambience: Dutch Landscape Painting in the Seventeenth
Century*, 1985, (Catalogue by Walter Liedtke), cat. no. 5, illus.

Literature:
C. Hofstede de Groot, *Catalogue Raisonné of the Works of the Most Eminent Dutch
Painters of the Seventeenth Century*, 1927, vol. VIII, p. 283, no. 1131
The Connoisseur, November 1959, p. 199, illus.
Apollo, October 1959, illus.
The Illustrated London News, November 21, 1959, illus.
The Connoisseur, June 1962, illus.
H. U. Beck, *Jan van Goyen*, 1973, vol. II, p. 416, no. 926, illus.

$180,000–220,000

16

*Jan van Goyen (1596–1656)

☐ 17   DELAPIDATED FARMHOUSE WITH FIGURES IN A LANDSCAPE

signed in monogram middle right and dated *1630*
oil on panel
14¼ by 20 in.   36 by 51 cm.

Provenance:
A. S. Drey, Munich
Willibald Duschnitz, Vienna
Central Art Collecting Point, Munich, until 1946, no. 6169
A. Brod, London, 1962
S. Nystad, The Hague, 1962
Sydney J. van den Bergh, Wassenaar
K. and V. Waterman, Amsterdam

Exhibited:
Leiden, Stedelijk Museum de Lakenhal, *Seventeenth Century Masters in Netherlands Private Collections*, 1965, no. 18, lent by Sydney J. van den Bergh
Amsterdam, Rijksmuseum, *Masters of 17th Century Dutch Landscape Painting*, October 2, 1987–January 3, 1988, Boston, Museum of Fine Arts, February 3–May 1, 1988, and Philadelphia, Museum of Art, June 5–July 31, 1988, pp. 323–324, cat. no. 34, illus. in color pl. 34 (entry by Peter C. Sutton; as dated 1630 or 1636)

Literature:
C. Hofstede de Groot, *Catalogue Raisonné of the Works of the Most Eminent Dutch Painters of the Seventeenth Century*, 1927, vol. VIII, p. 94, no. 385a (as dated 1639)
A. B. de Vries, "Old Masters in the Collection of Mr. and Mrs. Sydney J. van den Bergh," *Apollo*, 1964, vol. LXXX, p. 257 (as dated 1630)
A. B. de Vries, *Verzameling Sydney J. van den Bergh*, 1968, no. 46, illus. (as dated 1630)
H. U. Beck, *Jan van Goyen*, 1973, vol. II, no. 1141, illus. (as dated 1639 or 1630)
$80,000–120,000

17

*Frans Hals (1581/85–1666)

☐ 18   PORTRAIT OF A MAN

possibly indistinctly monogrammed upper center left
oil on canvas
31¼ by 23 in.   *79.5 by 58.4 cm.*

In a letter to Mr. Guterman dated October 1, 1984, Professor Seymour Slive states that having examined this picture first-hand after its 1974 restoration, which included removal of old disfiguring repaint, he believes it to be an original work by Frans Hals datable to the early or mid-1640's.

Provenance:
Konstanty Branicki, Paris, 1882
Count Xavier Branicki, Paris
Countess Rey, Chateau de Montresor (Sale: Sotheby's, London, March 26, 1969, no. 86, purchased by P. Truman)

Literature:
E. W. Moes, *Frans Hals, sa vie et son oeuvre*, 1909, no. 183
C. Hofstede de Groot, *Catalogue Raisonné of the Works of the Most Eminent Dutch Painters of the Seventeenth Century*, 1910, vol. III, p. 91, no. 319
Wilhelm v. Bode and M. J. Binder, *Frans Hals, sein Leben und seine Werke*, 1914, no. 205
W. R. Valentiner, *Frans Hals (Klassiker der Kunst)*, 1923, p. 200
Seymour Slive, *Frans Hals*, 1974, vol. III, p. 148, no. D56, fig. 177 (as possibly a copy of a lost original)

$700,000–900,000

*Jan Davidsz. de Heem (1606–1683/84)

□ 19   ELABORATE STILL LIFE OF FRUITS, MEAT PIE, CRUSTACEANS AND SILVER AND
GOLD OBJECTS, ALL ON A CLOTH-DRAPED TABLE

signed lower left and dated *J. De Heem F. A. 1649*
oil on canvas
29½ by 44 in.   75 by 111.5 cm.

Provenance:
E. H. Davenport, Esq., Davenport House, Bridgnorth, Shropshire, 1931, inher-
ited by his daughter, Mrs. Leicester-Warren, and removed from Davenport
House (Her sale: Christie's, London, June 12, 1931, lot 74, for 740 guineas,
purchased by Collings)
Mr. Alexander Jergens, Cincinnati, Ohio, 1931
French & Co., Inc., New York

Exhibited:
London, Whitechapel, St. Jude's, 1886, no. 138 (lent by E. H. Davenport)
Cincinnati, Museum of Art, on extended loan from Mr. Jergens
                                                    $1,800,000–2,400,000

2,500,000

19 *(detail)*

19 *(detail)*

*Meindert Hobbema (1638–1709)

☐ 20   ENTRANCE TO A WOOD WITH A FARM AND HORSEMEN
RIDING ON TWO ROADS

signed lower left
oil on panel
24½ by 34 in.   61 by 86.5 cm.

Provenance:
Phillips (Sale: London, 1826)
Count Pourtales, London (Sale: Phillips, London, May 19, 1826, lot 119, sold
for 420 guineas)
Lord Wharncliffe, 1835
John Smith, 1840
Kalkbrenner, Paris, 1842
Hope, 1855
Periere (Sale: Paris, March 6, 1872, no. 125)
Baron de Beuronville (Sale: Paris, May 9, 1881, no. 321)
A. Von Carstanjen, 1907
French & Co., Inc., New York

Exhibited:
Dusseldorf, 1904, no. 324
Munich, Alte Pinakothek, 1907–1938
Indianapolis Exhibition, 1937, no. 31
New York, Minskoff Cultural Center (to benefit the Appeal of Conscience
Foundation), *The Golden Ambience: Dutch Landscape Painting in the Seventeenth
Century,* 1985, (catalogue by Walter Liedtke), cat. no. 14, illus.

Literature:
John Smith, *Catalogue Raisonné of the Works of the Most Eminent, Dutch, Flemish,
and French Painters,* 1835, vol. VI, p. 131, no. 58
C. Hofstede de Groot, *Catalogue Raisonné of the Works of the Most Eminent Dutch
Painters of the Seventeenth Century,* 1912, vol. IV, no. 115
Georges Broulhiet, *Meindert Hobbema,* 1938, p. 388, no. 84, illus.

$400,000–600,000

20

*Pieter de Hooch (1629–1684)

□ 21   MUSICAL PARTY ON A TERRACE

signed in monogram lower right
oil on canvas
26¼ by 31 in.   67 by 79 cm.

This painting is dated by Peter Sutton (see literature below) *circa* 1667.

Provenance:
C. J. Nieuwenhuys (Sale: London, May 10, 1833, no. 34, sold for 85 guineas)
R. de Cornelissen (Sale: Brussels, May 11, 1857, no. 30)
M. Gilkinet (Sale: Paris, April 18, 1863, no. 27, sold for 2,900 francs, purchased by)
Vicomte de Buisseret (Sale: Brussels, April 29–30, 1891, no. 51, sold for 4,500 francs)
Charles Sedelmeyer, Paris, 1891, sold to
Baron Konigswarter, Vienna, 1891, resold to
Charles Sedelmeyer, Paris, 1892, sold to
C. D. Borden, New York, 1894 (Sale: New York, February 13–14, 1913, no. 25, illus., sold for $5,100, purchased by Knoedler)
M. Knoedler & Co., New York
Oscar Huldschinsky, Berlin, 1914 (Sale: Berlin, May 10, 1928, no. 15, purchased by Fischer)
Mrs. Paul H. Klingenstein, New York
Newhouse Galleries, New York

Exhibited:
Paris, Sedelmeyer Gallery, *One Hundred Paintings of Old Masters belonging to the Sedelmeyer Gallery,* 1894, no. 19, illus.
New York, The Metropolitan Museum of Art, *The Hudson-Fulton Celebration,* 1909, catalogue by W. R. Valentiner, vol. I, no. 57, illus.
Berlin, Kaiser Friedrich Museums, *Ausstellung von Werken alter Kunst aus dem Privatbesitz von Mitgliedern des Kaiser Friedrich Museums Vereins,* May 1914, no. 70

Literature:
C. J. Nieuwenhuys, *A Review of the Lives and Works of some of the Most Eminent Painters: with Remarks on the Opinions and Statements of Former Writers,* 1834, p. 153–156
John Smith, *Supplement to the Catalogue Raisonné of the Works of the Most Eminent Dutch, Flemish, and French Painters,* 1842, p. 567, no. 13
H. Havard III, *L'Art et les artistes hollandais,* 1880, p. 122
C. Hofstede de Groot, *Catalogue Raisonné of the Works of the Most Eminent Dutch Painters of the Seventeenth Century,* 1908, vol. I, p. 513–514, no. 136
W. R. Valentiner, "Die Austellung Hollandischer Gemalde in New York," *Monatschefte fur Kunstwissenschaft,* III, 1910, p. 9
W. R. Valentiner and A. F. Jaccaci, *Old and Modern Masters in the Collection of Mr. C. D. Borden,* 1911, pp. 14–15, 37, no. 4, illus.
Lionel Cust, "Notes on Pictures in the Royal Collection–XVIII," *The Burlington Magazine,* vol. XXV, July 1914, p. 205
American Art Annual, American Federation of Arts, New York, 1914, vol. XI, p. 439
E. Plietzsch, "Die Ausstellung von Werken alter Kunst in der Berliner KGL. Akademie der Kunst," *Zeitschrift fur Bildende Kunst* June 1914, p. 231
Arthur de Rudder, *Pieter de Hooch et son Oeuvre,* 1914, p. 105, no. 83, illus. opposite p. 80
C. H. Collins Baker, *Master of Painting, Pieter de Hooch,* 1925, p. 6
W. R. Valentiner, "Pieter de Hooch–Part One," *Art in America,* vol. 15, December 1926, pp. 47 and 63
W. R. Valentiner, "Pieter de Hooch–Part Two," *Art in America,* vol. 15, p. 70
Clotilde Briere-Misme, "Tableau Inedits ou peu connu de Pieter de Hooch," *Gazette des Beaux-Arts,* vol. XVI, November 1927, p. 272
W. R. Valentiner, *Pieter de Hooch, Klassiker der Kunst,* 1929, no. 148
Franzsepp Wurtenberger, *Das Hollandische Gesellschaftsbild,* 1937, p. 86
Peter Sutton, *Pieter de Hooch,* 1980, pp. 31, 32, 33, 99, cat. no. 76, illus. pl. 79

$250,000–350,000

*Jan Lievens (1607–1674)

□ 22   PORTRAIT OF REMBRANDT'S MOTHER

signed in monogram upper right
oil on panel
17 by 13¾ in.   43.5 by 35 in.

This painting may be dated *circa* 1629 on the basis of style.

In a letter dated October 17, 1987, Prof. Dr. Werner Sumowski confirms that the present painting, which he describes as a masterpiece of the early Lievens ("Ein hauptwerk des fruhen Lievens.") is identical with his no. 1261 in the *Rembrandt-Schüler* (see 1981 literature below). He points out that the histories of his nos. 1261 and 1262 were confused in the Braunschweig exhibition of 1979. In his 1980 work (see literature below), Sumowski describes the veil in the present painting as follows, ". . . der helle, buntgestickte Schleier ein Wunderwerk an Farbstufungen und Transparenzen." He further states in 1983 (see below) that while some previous scholars believed his no. 1262 to be the primary version of this composition, he considers the present picture to be the principal one.

Provenance:
Sale: L. Merens, Amsterdam, April 15, 1778, no. 92 (as by Rembrandt)
Cardinal Fesch, Rome (Sale: March 17, 1835, no. 193 (as Rembrandt)
J. F. Winterbottom, East Woodhay, Newbury, Berkshire, England (Sale: Messrs. Foster, London, Wednesday, April 27, 1870, lot 290 (as by Rembrandt, sale catalogue description, including mention of the Fesch provenance, is affixed to the reverse of the painting)
Earl of Levin and Melville (as Rembrandt)
Leggatt Bros., London, 1956 (as Rembrandt)
Oscar and Peter Johnson, London
K. and V. Waterman, Amsterdam

Exhibited:
Braunschweig, Herzog Anton Ulrich-Museum, *Jan Lievens: ein Maler im Schatten Rembrandts*, September 6–November 11, 1979, p. 70, no. 18, illus. p. 71 (with incorrect provenance and literature references)
Amsterdam, Waterman Gallery, *The Impact of a Genius: Rembrandt, his Pupils and Followers in the Seventeenth Century*, 1983, p. 192, no. 50, p. 193, illus., cat. by Albert Blankert, Ben Broos, Ernst van de Watering, Guido Jansen, and Willem van de Watering (loaned by Mr. Guterman)

Literature:
John Smith, *Catalogue Raisonné of the Works of the Most Eminent Dutch, Flemish, and French Painters*, 1836, Vol. VII, p. 185, no. 588 (as Rembrandt, engraved by J. J. Reinheimer)
C. Hofstede de Groot, *Catalogue Raisonné of the Works of the Most Eminent Dutch Painters of the Seventeenth Century*, 1916, Vol. VI, p. 259, no. 520, p. 328, no. 690e, p. 410, no. 894c (as Rembrandt)
Christopher Brown, *Burlington Magazine*, 1979 (Review of the Braunschweig exhibition), p. 742
Werner Sumowski, *Kunstchronik*, 1980 (Review of the Braunschweig exhibition), p. 9
Werner Sumowski, *Gemälde der Rembrandt-Schüler*, 1983, Vol. III, p. 1801, no. 1261, illus. p. 1900 in color

$80,000–120,000

*Philips Koninck (1619–1688)

☐ 23   EXTENSIVE RIVER LANDSCAPE WITH FIGURES
AND HERDS OF ANIMALS IN THE DISTANCE

oil on canvas
32½ by 44¼ in.   84 by 112.5 cm.

It is likely that a Philips Koninck *Landscape* of identical size as the present painting, now in the Metropolitan Museum of Art, New York (inv. no. 1980.4), is the pendant to this work. Both paintings were together in an English private collection (Whatman, according to an annotated catalogue in the Frick Art Reference Library, New York) until the 1900 sale (see provenance below), when they were sold as separate lots, numbers 59 and 60. Sumowski suggests a date in the mid 1660's; Liedtke proposes a date *circa* 1670.

Provenance:
Whatman (Sale: Christie's, London, June 16, 1900, no. 60, sold for 367 guineas, purchased by)
M. H. Colnaghi (Sale: London, November 19, 1908, no. 58, sold for 240 guineas)
Arthur M. Grenfell (Sale: Christie's, London, November 26, 1914, no. 18, sold for 892.10 guineas, purchased by Agnew)
H. J. Joel (Sale: Christie's, London, July 7, 1978, lot 131, illus.)
Leger Galleries, London
French & Co., Inc., New York

Exhibited:
New York, Minskoff Cultural Center (to benefit the Appeal of Conscience Foundation), *The Golden Ambience: Dutch Landscape Painting in the Seventeenth Century*, 1985, (catalogue by Walter Liedtke), cat. no. 15, illus.

Literature:
The Connoisseur, vol. 23, 1909, p. 63
H. Gerson, *Philips Koninck*, 1936, p. 108, no. 41
Werner Sumowski, *Gemälde der Rembrandt-Schüler*, 1983, vol. III, p. 1550, no. 1071, illus. p. 1621 (dated to the mid 1670's)

$450,000–650,000

*Johannes Lingelbach (1622–1674)

☐ 24   A SHEPHERD AND SHEPHERDESS WITH A HERD IN A PASTORAL LANDSCAPE

signed lower right
oil on canvas
17½ by 15¼ in.   *44.5 by 39 cm.*

Provenance:
Van Baaren, the Hague, before 1944
Sale: Sotheby's, New York, June 7, 1984, lot 11, illus.

$60,000–80,000

24

*Frans van Mieris, the Elder (1635–1681)

☐ 25   AN OLD WOMAN SINGING

signed upper left and dated *1677*
oil on panel
*original size: 6¼ by 4½ in.   16 by 11.25 cm. (the original panel has been set later
into a larger one measuring 7 by 5 in. [17.5 by 13 cm.])*

Provenance:
Count van Wassenaar-Obdam, The Hague (Sale: August 19, 1750, no. 52)
A. Dijkman (Sale: Amsterdam, July 17, 1794, lot 23)
Graf L. Sievers (Sale: Amsterdam, November 9, 1875, no. 47)
D. Koetser, 1968
Sale: Sotheby's, London, December 11, 1985, lot 96, illus.

Literature:
Gerard Hoet, *Catalogus of Naamlyst van Schilderyen*, 1752, vol. II, p. 293, no. 53
C. Hofstede de Groot, *Verzeichnis der Werke der her Vorragendsten Hollandischen
Maler des XVII Jahrhunderts*, 1928, vol. X, p. 42, nos. 161 and p. 50, no. 196
Otto Naumann, *Frans Van Mieris*, 1981, vol. II, p. 160, no. C89a, and p. 208,
no. D103; illus. vol. I, fig. 117 (captioned erroneously as the Hammer collection
copy)

$50,000–70,000

25 *(actual size)*

*Willem van Mieris (1662–1747)

☐ 26   A SOLDIER SMOKING A PIPE (POSSIBLY A SELF-PORTRAIT)

oil on panel
6 by 4¾ in.   15.5 by 12 cm.

Pieter de la Court (see provenance below) was the patron of Willem van Mieris. He commissioned the artist to make this painting, together with several others, after compositions by his father, Frans van Mieris. The present picture is recorded in the De la Court inventories of 1731, 1739 and 1749, before being sold in 1766. Willem's copies were highly regarded and Allard de la Court even wrote that they were so good they were, ". . . largely taken as the originals," (see Fock literature below, p. 265).

On the back of the panel is the seal of Ricquier, notary in Rouen who organized the Warneck sale. Like the original, this picture had a pendant, portrait of the artist's wife, which was with it until 1922 in the Warneck collection, but does not appear in the sale. It is now in the Assheton Bennett collection in the Manchester City Art Gallery.

Provenance:
Pieter de La Court, Leyden, before 1731 (Sale: September 8, 1766, lot 8, as Frans van Mieris, for 100 florins, purchased by J. van de Velde)
J. Vliet (Sale: Amsterdam, October 12, 1774, lot 138, as Frans van Mieris)
B. Ocke (Sale: Leyden, April 21, 1817, lot 77, as Frans van Mieris, for 122 florins, purchased by Smart, with its pendant)
V. J. von Adlerstein (Sale: Vienna, May 27, 1828, lot 104)
Robert de Saint Victor (Sale: November 26, 1922, lot 53, as Willem van Mieris)
E. Warneck (Sale: Paris, May 27, 1926, lot 56, as Frans van Mieris)
M. Lange (Sale: Paris, May 24, 1935, lot 74, as Frans van Mieris)
Sale: Palais Galliera, Paris, November 29, 1965, lot 118 (as Frans van Mieris)
Sale: Palais Galliera, Paris, December 7, 1967, lot 146 (as Willem van Mieris)
Brian Koester, London, 1968, cat. no. 44, illus.
Sale: Sotheby's, London, December 11, 1985, lot 97, illus. (The Property of a Nobleman)

Literature:
J. C. Overvoorde, "De collectie De La Court", *Leids Jaarboekje*, vol. V, 1908, p. 20
T. von Frimmel, *Lexikon de Wiener Gemäldesammlungen*, 1913, p. 44 (Alderstein collection)
C. Hofstede de Groot, *Beschreibendes und kritisches Verzeichnis der Werke der hervorragendsten Hollandischen Maler des XVII Jahrhunderts*, 1928, vol. X, p. 30, under no. 103 (as a copy of a Frans van Mieris), p. 174, no. 261 (as Willem van Mieris)
H. van Hall, *Portretten van Netherlandse Beeldende Kunstenaars*, 1963, p. 211
Otto Naumann, *Frans van Mieris*, 1981, p. 51, no. 43a, illus. fig. 43a (as a copy by Willem van Mieris after Frans van Mieris, possibly a self-portrait)
C. Willemijn Fock, "Willem van Mieris en zijn mecenas Pieter de la Court van der Voort", *Leids Kunsthistorisch Jaarboek*, 1984, pp. 264–265, fig. 4

$40,000–60,000

26 *(actual size)*

*Adriaen van Ostade (1610–1685)

□ 28   OLD MAN SMOKING A PIPE

signed lower right
oil on panel
9 by 7¼ in.   23 by 18.5 cm.

Provenance:
Meiffre ainé (Sale: Paris, February 25, 1845, no. 67, purchased by Cousin)
Baron de Varange (Sale: Paris, May 26, 1852, no. 30, 580 francs)
Baron de Varange (Sale: Paris, April 25, 1857, no. 9, sold for 1500 francs)
Duc de Staepole (Sale: Drouot, Paris, March 14, 1890, no. 31, purchased by Villeneuve)
Montaignac, January 1893
Charles Sedelmeyer, Paris, January 1893
Baron Königswarter, February 1893
Charles Sedelmeyer, Paris, 1894, *Catalogue of 100 Paintings of Old Masters*, p. 34, no. 28, illus. p. 35
G. Eissler, Vienna, September 1900
J. Camberlyn a.o. (a.o. Alfred Schindler, Vienna)
Sale: Frederik Muller, Amsterdam, July 13, 1926, no. 672, illus., purchased by Spanjaard
Wetzlar, 1959
Charles Roelofsz, Amsterdam

Exhibited:
Laren NH, Singer Museum, *Kunstschatten*, 1959, no. 65 (lent by Wetzlar)

Literature:
C. Hofstede de Groot, *Catalogue Raisonné of the Works of the Most Eminent Dutch Painters of the Seventeenth Century*, 1910, vol. III, p. 198, no. 190

$60,000–80,000

28

*Willem de Poorter (1608–after 1648)

☐ 29   TOBIAS AND THE ANGEL

oil on panel
20¾ by 27¼ in.   52.5 by 69.5 cm.

Prof. Werner Sumowski, in a letter dated October 30, 1985, has identified the present painting as a work by Willem de Poorter, datable to the early 1640's. Furthermore, he has included it as such in the forthcoming next volume of his *Gemälde der Rembrandt-Schüler* series as cat. no. 1613.

Provenance:
William Smith, sold to Emmerson in 1819 for 105 pounds
George Morant, London, purchased for 315 pounds (Sale: Phillips, London, May 18–21, 1832, lot 60, as G. Dow, for 231 pounds)
Thomas Lister, Baron Ribblesdale, London
D. Katz, Dieren, 1939
J. Walter, 1941
Marquess of Lothian (Sale: Sotheby's, London, June 24, 1970, lot 94, illus., as by Gerrit Dou)
K. and V. Waterman, Amsterdam

Exhibited:
Amsterdam, Rijksmuseum, *Bijbelsche kunst*, July 8–October 8, 1939, cat. no. 681 (as Gerrit Dou)

Literature:
John Smith, *Catalogue Raisonné of the Works of the Most Eminent Dutch, Flemish, and French Painters*, 1829, Vol. I, p. 44, no. 135 (as by Gerrit Dou)
W. Martin, *Het Leven en de werken van Gerrit Dou . . .*, 1901, p. 183, no. 2 (as Gerrit Dou)
C. Hofstede de Groot, *Catalogue Raisonné of the Works of the Most Eminent Dutch Painters of the Seventeenth Century*, 1908, vol. 1, p. 343, no. 2 (as Gerrit Dou)
W. Martin, *Gerard Dou, Sa vie et son oeuvre*, 1911, p. 163, no. 2 (as Gerrit Dou)
W. Martin, *Gerard Dou (Klassiker de Kunst)*, 1913, p. 179, illus. p. 1 (as Gerrit Dou, the composition similar to the work of Poorter)

$50,000–70,000

*Adam Pynacker (1622–1673)

☐ 30   ITALIANATE MOUNTAINOUS RIVER LANDSCAPE WITH BOATS, ANIMALS, AND
       FIGURES

signed lower center
oil on panel
23¾ by 36¼ in.   60.5 by 92 cm.

This painting was included in Dr. Laurie B. Harwood's doctoral dissertation
on Pynacker for the Courtauld Institute, and will be included in her forthcoming monograph on the artist now in preparation for Davaco Publishers.

Provenance:
M. Langlier, 1768
W. Smith
The Marquess of Lansdowne, Bowood, no. 150
Lady Colum Crichton-Stuart, formerly wife of the Sixth Marquess of
Lansdowne
Lady Elizabeth Mary Lambton, second daughter of the Sixth Marquess of
Lansdowne, thence by descent to
A Lady (Sale: Christie's, London, July 8, 1977, lot 72)
French & Co., New York

Exhibited:
London, Royal Acadamy, *Dutch Paintings: 1450–1750*, 1952, no. 477
New York, Richard L. Feigen & Co., *Landscape Painting in Rome, 1595–1675*,
January 30–March 23, 1985 (catalogue by Ann Sutherland Harris), p. 252,
cat. no. 41, illus. (lent by Mr. and Mrs. Guterman)
New York, Minskoff Cultural Center (to benefit the Appeal of Conscience
Foundation), *The Golden Ambience: Dutch Landscape Painting in the Seventeenth
Century*, 1985, (catalogue by Walter Liedtke), cat. no. 22, illus.

Literature:
John Smith, *Catalogue Raisonné of the Works of the Most Eminent Dutch, Flemish,
and French Painters*, 1835, vol. VI, p. 288, no. 6
Mrs. Jameson, *Companion to the Most Celebrated Picture Galleries of Art in London*,
1844, no. 73
Dr. Waagen, *Treasures of Art in Great Britain*, 1854, vol. III, p. 165
G. E. Ambrose, *Catalogue of the Collection of Pictures Belonging to the Marquess of
Lansdowne*, 1898, p. 78
C. Hofstede de Groot, *Beschreibendes und kritisches Verzeichnis der Werke der hervor-
ragendsten Holländischen Maler des XVII Jahrhunderts*, 1926, vol. IX, p. 533, no. 139
$140,000–160,000

*Salomon Rombouts (before 1652–after 1702)

□ 31   THE ENCAMPMENT

signed lower right
oil on panel
24½ by 33½ in.   *62 by 85 cm.*

Provenance:
The Earl of Strathmore, England
Gebr. Douwes, Amsterdam

$40,000–60,000

31

*Jacob van Ruisdael (1628/29–1682)

☐ 32   WOODED MOUNTAINOUS LANDSCAPE

signed in monogram lower right
oil on canvas
38¾ by 49½ in.   98.5 by 125.5 cm.

This picture probably dates from about 1650, and it has been suggested that the figures were added by Johannes Lingelbach who returned from Rome to Amsterdam in the summer of 1650.

Provenance:
Lady Elizabeth Pringle, 1877
Charles Sedelmeyer, Paris, *Catalogue of 300 Paintings*, 1898, pp. 196–197, no. 175, illus.
P. C. Hanford, Chicago (Sale: American Art Association, New York, January 30, 1902)
Sale: Sotheby's, New York, June 7, 1984, lot 76, illus.

Exhibited:
London, Royal Academy, *Winter Exhibition*, 1877, no. 25
New York, Minskoff Cultural Center (to benefit the Appeal of Conscience Foundation), *The Golden Ambience: Dutch Landscape Painting in the Seventeenth Century*, 1985 (catalogue by Walter Liedtke), cat. no. 10, illus.

Literature:
C. Hofstede de Groot, *Catalogue Raisonné of the Works of the Most Eminent Dutch Painters of the Seventeenth Century*, 1912, vol. IV, pp. 204 and 206, nos. 645 and 652
K. E. Simon, *Jacob van Ruisdael*, 1927, p. 75
Jacob Rosenberg, *Jacob van Ruisdael*, 1928, no. 412

$500,000–700,000

bought in

*Salomon van Ruysdael (1600/03–1670)

☐ 33   NIJMEGEN WITH THE VALKHOF AND A FERRY CROSSING THE RIVER WAAL

signed in monogram and dated *1652* on the ferry
oil on panel
27½ by 36¼ in.   69.5 by 92 cm.

The Valkhof was a castle founded by Charlemagne (742–814) by the river
Waal at Nijmegen; it was largely torn down in 1796. A full history of this
structure is recorded in: Peter Schepenbeek, *Het Valkhof*, 1961.

Provenance:
Lord Ennismore, 1st Earl of Listowel, Kingston House, Knightsbridge, ac-
quired 1800–1815 (Sale: Christie's, London, July 8, 1983, lot 7, illus.)
John Mitchell and Son, London

Exhibited:
New York, Minskoff Cultural Center (to benefit the Appeal of Conscience
Foundation), *The Golden Ambience: Dutch Landscape Painting in the Seventeenth
Century,* 1985 (catalogue by Walter Liedtke), cat. no. 7, illus.

$400,000–600,000

907,500

*Pieter Jansz. Saenredam (1597–1665)

☐ 34   THE TOWN HALL AT HAARLEM

oil on panel
15½ by 19½ in.   39.5 by 49.5 cm.

Both Walter Lietdtke and Gary Schwartz (in collaboration with Marten Jan Bok) will be including the present painting in their respective monographs on Saenredam. The painting shows the facade of the Town Hall as it was before 1630 when Salomon de Bray remodelled it and, *a fortiori*, before the 1633 rebuilding of the balcony. The Town Hall is depicted in the same form, but from a more distant viewpoint, in an etching by Jan van de Velde inscribed: *P. Zaenredam Inuent*, which appears as an illustration in S. Ampzing's *Beschrijvinge ende Lof van de Stad Haerlem* published in 1628. A drawing of 1749 by Hendrik Spilman after the present painting (in the Haarlem archives) is inscribed: *Afbeelding van 't Stadhuis te Haarlem Ao. 1630. P. Saenredam Pinx.* In the Enschedé sale of 1786 (see provenance below) the painting is described as by "P. P. Saenredam 1630." For all the foregoing reasons it seems probable that the picture was painted in or near 1630 and this dating is supported by the costume of the figures.

There is a preparatory drawing by Saenredam for this picture, without the figures, in the Fodor Museum, Amsterdam.

The first mention of this painting is as in the collection (ca. 1765) of a Haarlem printer, Johannes Enschedé, who owned also at least two drawings, and probably another painting, by Saenredam. In English nineteenth century sales and a 1903 exhibition the picture was wrongly attributed to the then better known Gerrit Berckheyde (1638–1698) who did in fact paint the Town Hall in its altered form, but quite apart from the style, this attribution is excluded by the costume of the figures which is obviously of a period before the birth of Berckheyde.

The attribution by Gudlaugsson of the figures to Pieter Post seems justified by comparison with such of Post's paintings as two military scenes of 1631 in the Mauritshuis. In a letter of April 3, 1986, Liedtke agrees with Gudlauggson's earlier suggestion that the figures are by Post. These figures have also been given to Saenredam himself (e.g. in the catalogue of the Brussels exhibition, *Dessins hollandais du Siècle d'Or*, 1961, p. 36).

Provenance:
Johannes Enschedé, Haarlem, c. 1765 (according to Nagler—see literature below, Sale: Haarlem, May 30, 1786, lot 11, as "P. P. Saenredam 1630")
Van Leyden, Amsterdam (Sale: Paris, July 5, postponed to November 5–7, 1804, lot 81, as Saenredam)
Sale: Amsterdam, April 24, 1838, lot 50 (as Saenredam), purchased by Chapuis
Sir Maziere Brady, Bart., Dublin (Sale: London, July 1, 1871, lot 123, as Berckheyde, purchased by Bohn)
Henry G. Bohn (Sale: London, March 20, 1885, lot 189, as G. Berckheyde, purchased by Bischoffsheim)
Henry Louis Bischoffsheim, Bute House, London (died 1908)
P. Lugt, Brussels (lent to Haarlem Museum 1933–45)
J. R. Bier, Haarlem

continued

34

lot 34 continued

M. Franck, New York, 1949–51
Wildenstein, New York, by 1954, sold to
J. C. H. Heldring, Oosterbeek, 1959 (Sale: Sotheby's, London, March 27, 1963, lot 18)
Sale: Sotheby's, London, December 12, 1984, lot 62, illus. (as Saenredam)

Exhibited:
London, Corporation Art Gallery (Guildhall), *Works by Painters of the Dutch School*, 1903, no. 140 (as Gerrit Berckheyde)
Haarlem, Frans Hals Museum, on loan 1933–45 (as Saenredam)
Rotterdam, Boymans Museum, *Pieter Jansz, Saenredam*, 1937–38, no. 4 (as Saenredam)
Amsterdam, Fodor Museum, *Pieter Jansz. Saenredam*, 1938, no. 4 (as Saenredam)
London (Ontario), University of West Ontario, *17th Century Dutch Masters*, 1954 (as Saenredam)
Oslo, National Gallery, *Fra Rembrandt til Vermeer*, 1959, no. 65, illus. (as Saenredam)
Utrecht, Central Museum, *Collectie J.C.H. Heldring*, 1960, no. 33, illus. pl. 27 (as Saenredam)
Utrecht, Central Museum, *Pieter Jansz. Saenredam*, 1961, no. 86, illus. fig. 88 (as Saenredam)

Literature:
G. K. Nagler, *Neues Allgemeines Kunstler-Lexikon*, 1845, vol. XVI, p. 80 (as Saenredam)
P. T. A. Swillens, *Pieter Jansz. Saenredam*, 1935, pp. 9, 59, no. 226, illus. fig. 56 (as Saenredam)
N. S. Trivas, "Pieter Saenredam," *Apollo*, 1938, vol. XXVII, p. 155, no. 155 (as Saenredam)
S. J. Gudlaugsson, "Aanvullingen omtrent Pieter Posts werkzaamheid als schilder," *Oud-Holland*, 1954, vol. LXIX, esp. p. 68, illus. p. 67, fig. 11 (as Saenredam with figures by Pieter Post)
Weltkunst, September 15, 1960, illus. p. 8 (as Saenredam)
Catalogue raisonne van der Werken van Pieter Jansz. Saenredam . . . ., 2nd revised ed., 1961, pp. 129–132 (as Saenredam)

$350,000–450,000

34 *(detail)*

*Herman Saftleven (1609–1685)

☐ 35 EXTENSIVE RHINELAND LANDSCAPE WITH FIGURES, ANIMALS, AND BOATS
WITH A VILLAGE ON A CLIFF

signed lower left and dated *1650*
oil on canvas
21 by 28 in.   53 by 71 cm.

Provenance:
De Heer en Mervrouw R. E. J. van de Loo-van Ryckevorsel van Kessel,
Amsterdam
A. van der Meer, Amsterdam, 1963, cat. no. 14, illus.

Exhibited:
Dordrecht, Dordrechts Museum, *Zee-River-en Oevergezichten: Nederlandse schil-
derijn uit de zeventiende eeuw,* July 12–September 14, 1964, no. 69, illus. fig. 62
New York, Minskoff Cultural Center (to benefit the Appeal of Conscience Foundation), *The Golden Ambience: Dutch Landscape Painting in the Seventeenth Century,*
1985 (catalogue by Walter Liedtke), cat. no. 16, illus.
Amsterdam, Rijksmuseum, *Masters of 17th Century Dutch Landscape Painting,*
October 2, 1987–January 3, 1988, Boston, Museum of Fine Arts, February
3–May 1, 1988 and Philadelphia, Museum of Art, June 5–July 31, 1988, cat.
no. 97, illus. in color pl. 32 (entry by Peter C. Sutton)

Literature:
Weltkunst, November 1, 1963, illus. p. 100
W. Schulz, *Herman Saftleven,* 1982, p. 141, no. 64

$100,000–150,000

*Godfried Schalken (1643–1706)

□ 36   BOY BLOWING CHARCOAL TO LIGHT A CANDLE

signed lower center
oil on canvas
29½ by 25 in.   75 by 63.5 cm.

Provenance:
Probably bought from the artist by Robert Spencer, 2nd Earl Sunderland (1641–1702), Althorp
Charles, 3rd Earl Sunderland (1675–1722)
The Hon. John Spencer (1708–1746)
John, 1st Earl Spencer (1734–1783), thence by descent to the present Earl Spencer
Johnny van Haeften, Ltd., London

Exhibited:
Leeds, *Fine Art Exhibition*, 1868, no. 696
London, Royal Academy, *Dutch Pictures 1450–1750*, 1952–53, no. 595

Literature:
George Vertue, *Note Book, A.q.*, 1731–36 (British Museum Add. Ms. 23071)
George Knapton, *Catalogue of the Pictures at Althorpe and Wimbledon belonging to the late Honorable Mr. Spencer*, 1746, no. 381
A Catalogue of the Pictures of Althorp, 1750 (as in the Yellow Bedchamber)
John Smith, *Catalogue Raisonné of the Works of the Most Eminent Dutch, Flemish, and French Painters*, 1833, vol. IV, p. 287, no. 101
C. Hofstede de Groot, *Catalogue Raisonné of the Works of the Most Eminent Dutch Painters of the Seventeenth Century*, 1913, vol. V, p. 377, no. 227
Horace Walpole, "Journal of Visits to Country Seats etc., 1760," *Walpole Society*, vol. XVI, 1928
William Bray, *Sketch of a Tour into Derbyshire and Yorkshire*, 1778 (2nd edition 1783, p. 731)
Catalogue of the Pictures at Althorp, November 1802 (as in the Drawing Room)
T. F. Dibdin, *Aedes Althorpianae*, 1822, p. 17
Jacques Thuillier, *L'Opera Completa di George de la Tour*, 1973, p. 100, under no. D15, which is a copy attributed to La Tour in the Lyman Alleyn Museum, New London, Connecticut, after "l'originale, firmato da Schalken, e conservato a Althorp House" ("the original, signed by Schalken, and located at Althorp House")
Benedict Nicolson and Christopher Wright, *Georges de la Tour*, 1974, p. 205, under no. 15, *A Boy blowing a Firebrand*, Lyman Alleyn Museum, London, Connecticut, "This is a copy of the Schalken at Althorp."
K. J. Garlick, "A Catalogue of Pictures at Althorp," *Walpole Society*, vol. XLV, 1976 (in which the above mentioned Althorp inventories of 1746, 1750, and 1802 are published), p. 76, no. 585

$80,000–120,000

AUTHORSHIP: Ascribed to the named artist—subject to the qualifications set forth in the Glossary and Conditions of Sale, front of this Catalogue.

39

*Hendrick Terbrugghen (1588–1629)

☐ 39 A MAN PLAYING A THERBO and A MAN PLAYING A VIOLA DA BRACCIO:
A PAIR OF PAINTINGS

both signed in monogram and indistinctly dated possibly *1622*, one lower
right, the other lower left
both oil on canvas
each: 26½ by 22¾ in. 67.5 by 58 cm.

Provenance:
Pootjes, Ardenhout, Holland
Christophe Janet, New York

$300,000–400,000

39

*Daniel Jansz. Thievaert (before 1613–before 1658)

☐ 40   THE LABORER OF GIBEA OFFERING HOSPITALITY TO THE LEVITE
AND HIS WIFE

signed lower left
oil on canvas
63¾ by 74 in.   162 by 188 cm.

Provenance:
Johnny van Haeften, Ltd., London

Exhibited:
New York, Metropolitan Museum of Art, 1985, temporary loan (lent by Mr.
and Mrs. Guterman)

$50,000–70,000

acquired by MFA. Boston, 1988
offered to NGh for £5000 !

*Jan Jansz. den Uyl (1595/96–1639/40)

☐ 41   STILL LIFE OF A JUG, AN OVERTURNED TAZZA, A TALL GLASS, A WATER GLASS, AND THREE PLATES WITH CURRANTS, OLIVES, A PARTIALLY PEELED LEMON, AND A KNIFE ALL ON A TABLE WITH A WHITE CLOTH

signed with an owl on the bottom of the tablecloth and dated *1633* on the handle of the jug
oil on panel
35½ by 28¼ in.   90 by 72 cm.

As Ingvar Bergstrom notes (see literature below), the present painting is extraordinary for its unusual compositional daring: the placement of all the main elements in the left side of the picture, with balance achieved only through the strong architectural elements in the right half, ". . . was something entirely new and unconventional in still-life art in the year 1633."

Also remarkable is Den Uyl's sensitive use of color and light, a testament to his skill in the monochrome tradition of still life painting. His care with detail, such as the depiction of scratches and dents on the surface of the silver, is again outstanding. As Bergstrom comments concerning the present painting, "This work alone would be enough to secure for Den Uyl a reputation as one of Holland's foremost still-life painters. It gives a sincere impression of granduer, reveals a forceful and virile temperament, and explains the high esteem in which he was held by his contemporaries; indeed three of his paintings found a place in Rubens's collection."

Provenance:
C. F. Bugge (Sale: Copenhagen, August 21, 1837, no. 127)
Den Moltke (Sale: Winkel and Magnussen, sale no. 96, June 1, 1931, no. 50)
Niels Olesen, Copenhagen
Mrs. Asta Olesen, Copenhagen (Sale: Rasmussen, Copenhagen, May 2, 1984, lot 20, illus.)
French & Co., Inc., New York

Exhibited:
Copenhagen, Royal Museum of Fine Arts, *Mit Bedst Kunstvaerk*, October 1941, no. 85
Copenhagen, *Stilleben*, Kunstforeningen 1965, no. 84

continued

2,200,000

lot 41 continued

Literature:
Dansk Kunstblad II, June 24, 1837, no. 84
N. Hoyen, *Fortegnelse over Den Moltkeske Malerisamling*, 1856, no. 83 (under Boelema)
Karl Madsen, *Tilskueren*, no. 14, 1897, p. 132
P. de Bocr, "J. J. den Uyl," *Oud Holland*, 1940, vol. LVII, pp. 49–64, no. 7
Kal Flor, *Mit Bedst Kunstvaerk*, 1941, pl. 17
Kunst i Privat Eje, 1944, vol. II, p. 94
N. R. A. Vroom, *De Schilders van het Monochrome Banketje*, 1945, p. 153, no. 278
Ingvar Bergstrom, *Hollandskt Stilleben-Maler under 1600–Talet*, 1947, p. 151, pl. 3, fig. 128
Ingvar Bergstrom, *Still-Life Painting*, 1956, pp. 144–153, pl. 4, fig. 129
Poul Gammelbo, *Dutch Still-Life Painting from the 16th to the 18th Centuries in Danish Collections*, 1960, p. 58, no. 62
N. R. A. Vroom, *A Modest Message as intimated by the painters of the Monochrome Banketje*, 1980, vol. II, p. 127, no. 657, illus.

$700,000–900,000

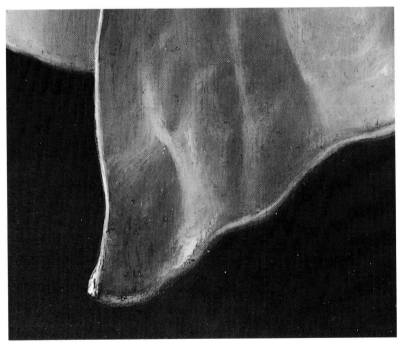

41 *(detail of signature)*

41 *(detail)*

*Lucas van Valckenborch (before 1535–1597)

☐ 42   AN ELEGANT PARTY DANCING IN THE COURTYARD OF A PALACE
WITH OTHER COUPLES IN A GARDEN, A CASTLE ATOP A HILL BEYOND

oil on panel
17¾ by 57½ in.   45 by 146 cm.

Provenance:
Sale: Sotheby's, New York, January 21, 1982, lot 100, illus.

$60,000–80,000

*AUTHORSHIP: Ascribed to the named artist—subject to the qualifications set forth in
the Glossary and Conditions of Sale, front of this Catalogue.

42

*Esaias van de Velde (1587–1630)

☐ 43   RIDERS ON A ROAD TO THE LEFT OF A POOL AND A RUINED TOWER

signed lower left and dated *1619*
oil on panel
11¼ by 14¼ in.   28.5 by 36 cm.

Provenance:
Sale: Sotheby's, London, April 19, 1972, lot 109, purchased by A. Brod, London
Dr. Eberhard Ernst, Munich
K. and V. Waterman, Amsterdam

Exhibited:
New York, Minskoff Cultural Center (to benefit the Appeal of Conscience
Foundation), *The Golden Ambience: Dutch Landscape Painting in the Seventeenth
Century*, 1985, (catalogue by Walter Liedtke), cat. no. 3, illus.

Literature:
George S. Keyes, *Esaias van de Velde, 1587–1630*, 1984, p. 155, no. 131, pl. 83,
colorplate IX

$70,000–90,000

*Jan Victors (1619/20–ca. 1676)

☐ 44   RUTH AND NAOMI

signed middle right and dated *1653*
oil on canvas
42¾ by 54 in.   108.5 by 137 cm.

Debra Miller, in her 1985 article and doctoral dissertation on the works of Jan Victors (see literature below), suggests that the present painting ("one of Jan Victors' finest works") has a probable pendant in Victors's *Esau and the Mess of Pottage* in the Gallery at Lazienki, Budapest. Of identical size and also dated *1653*, she points out that there is not only a compositional similarity in the close-range, half-length figures, but a thematic similarity as well in the portrayal of, "the fundamental Old Testament theme of the propogation of the unalterable male line of descendency from Abraham."

As Dr. Miller discusses, "Victors' specific episode of Ruth swearing her allegiance to Naomi is recounted in Ruth 1. The narrative tells of the relationship between Naomi of Bethlehem and her two Moabite daughters-in-law, Orpah and Ruth. After the three women became widowed, Naomi determined that her daughters-in-law should return to the homes of their mothers. Orpah departed, but the steadfast Ruth refused to forsake her mother-in-law. Naomi prodded: 'Behold, thy sister-in-law is gone back unto her people, and unto her gods: return thou after thy sister-in-law. And Ruth said, Intreat me not to leave thee . . . for whither thou goest, I will go; and where thou lodgest, I will lodge: thy people shall be my people, and thy God my God' (Ruth 1:15–16)."

This painting will be included in Prof. Werner Sumowski's forthcoming fourth volume of the *Gemälde der Rembrandt-Schüler*, as cat. no. 1767, illus. in color.

Provenance:
possibly Sale: Amsterdam 15, 1825, no. 88
Girot, Antwerp, circa 1950
Sale: Mak van Waay, Amsterdam, October 31, 1967, no. 515, illus. (as Vertumnus and Pomona)
Hoogsteder–Naumann, Ltd., New York

Exhibited:
New York, Metropolitan Museum of Art, 1985, temporary loan (lent by Mr. and Mrs. Guterman)

Literature:
Debra Miller, *Johannes Victors*, 1985, Ph.D. Dissertation, University of Delaware, pp. 178 and 303, cat. no. 67
Debra Miller, "Ruth and Naomi of 1653: an unpublished painting by Jan Victors," *Mercury*, 1985, no. 2, pp. 19–28, illus. fig. 1

$60,000–80,000

*David Vinckboons (1576–1629/32)

☐ 45 THE BLIND HURDY-GURDY PLAYER WITH A CROWD OF CHILDREN

signed upper right and dated *1609*
oil on panel
9¼ by 12½ in.   *23.5 by 31.5 cm.*

Provenance:
J. Leegenhoek, Paris
Henri Leroux, Versailles
Johnny van Haeften, Ltd., London

Literature:
K. Goossens, *D. Vinckboons*, 1954, p. 103, fig. 55
Georges Marlier, *Pierre Brueghel le Jeune*, 1969, p. 366, no. 4, fig. 226
                                                    $60,000–80,000

*Philips Wouwermans (1619–1668)

☐ 46 EXTENSIVE MOUNTAINOUS RIVER LANDSCAPE
WITH HORSEMEN WAITING FOR A FERRY

signed lower left and dated *1649*
oil on canvas
25¾ by 31¼ in.   65.5 by 79.5 cm.

In a letter dated August 5, 1983, Dr. Frederick Duparc notes that the present painting is one of the few dated Wouwermans pictures. He further comments that 1649 is his best documented year, as there are four dated works in that period.

Provenance:
Sale: Amsterdam, August 9, 1739, no. 4 (Hoet I, p. 596)
Empress Catherine II, acquired in the 1770's (Hermitage cat. 1774, no. 531)
Hermitage Palace, St. Petersburg, cat. 1870, no. 1016; also cats. of 1895, 1901 and 1916
Sale: Helbing, Frankfurt am Main, May 3, 1931, no. 122
Sale: Sotheby's, London, July 23, 1982, no. 10
French & Co., Inc., New York

Exhibited:
New York, Minskoff Cultural Center (to benefit the Appeal of Conscience Foundation), *The Golden Ambience: Dutch Landscape Painting in the Seventeenth Century*, 1985, (catalogue by Walter Liedtke), cat. no. 17, illus.
Amsterdam, Rijksmuseum, *Masters of 17th Century Dutch Landscape Painting*, October 2, 1987–January 3, 1988, Boston, Museum of Fine Arts, February 3–May 1, 1988 and Philadelphia, Museum of Fine Art, June 5–July 31, 1988, cat. no. 119, illus. in color pl. 91 (entry by Alan Chong)

Literature:
G. Hoet, *Catalogus of Naamlyst van Schilderyen*, 1752, vol. I, p. 596
Lacrois, 1861–1862, vol. XIII, p. 246
G. Waagen, *Die Gemäldesammlung in der Kaiserlichen Ermitage zu St. Petersberg*, 1864, p. 217
U. Thieme and F. Becker, *Allgemeines Lexikon der Bildenden Künstler*, 1947, vol. XXXVI, p. 267
C. Hofstede de Groot, *Catalogue Raisonné of the Works of the Most Eminent Dutch Painters of the Seventeenth Century*, 1909, vol. II, p. 358, nos. 362 and 363

$80,000–120,000

46

*Philips Wouwermans (1619–1668)

☐ 47   HORSEMEN, WASHERWOMEN, AND VARIOUS ANIMALS BY A RIVER
WITH A HORSE CART AND A COTTAGE IN THE DISTANCE

oil on canvas
24 by 33½ in.   61 by 85 cm.

Provenance:
S. Woodburn (Sale: London, June 24, 1853, for 190 pounds, purchased by
Gritten)
Earl of Egmont, Esq.
Rosenburg
R. H. Ward
Stig. Ahlstrom of Skara

Literature:
C. Hofstede de Groot, *Catalogue Raisonné of the Works of the Most Eminent Dutch
Painters of the Seventeenth Century,* 1928, vol. X, p. 370, no. 413a
$80,000–120,000

END OF SALE

47

International auction locations and representatives

UNITED KINGDOM & IRELAND

Salesrooms

London
34-35 New Bond Street,
London W1A 2AA and
Bloomfield Place
(off New Bond Street)
Telephone: 44 (1) 493-8080
Telex: 24454 SPBLON G

Chester
R. B. Allen
Booth Mansion,
28 Watergate Street,
Chester, Cheshire CH1 2NA
Telephone: 44 (244) 315531
Telex: 61577 SOBART G

Sussex
W. L. Weller, F.R.I.C.S., F.S.V.A.
Summers Place,
Billingshurst,
Sussex RH14 9AD
Telephone: 44 (40 381) 3933
Telex: 87210 GAVEL

Offices & Representatives

Cambridgeshire
Christopher Myers
56 High Street, Trumpington,
Cambridge CB2 2LS
Telephone: 44 (223) 845222

Devon & Cornwall
John Tremlett
Telephone: 44 (392) 833416

Gloucestershire
John Harvey
18 Imperial Square, Cheltenham
Gloucestershire, GL50 1QZ
Telephone: 44 (242) 510500

New Hampshire & Dorset
George Kidner
42 Holdenhurst Road,
Bournemouth, Dorset BH8 8AF
Telephone: 44 (202) 294425
Mary Fagan
Telephone: 44 (256) 780591

Lancashire
Susan Yorke
Telephone: 44 (200) 41520

Lincolnshire
Lady Victoria Leatham
George Archdale
The George Hotel Mews,
Station Road
Stamford, Lincolnshire PE9 2LB
Telephone: 44 (780) 51666

North of England
Matthew Festing
11 Osborne Terrace, Jesmond
Newcastle-upon-Tyne NE2 1NE
Telephone: 44 (91) 281 8867

The Earl of Carlisle, M.C., F.R.I.C.S.
Telephone: 44 (69 77) 3666

Somerset
Robert Dalgety
Magdalene House
Magdalene Street,
Taunton, Somerset TA1 1SB
Telephone: 44 (823) 288441

Suffolk
The Lord Cranworth
Telephone: 44 (47 335) 581

Warwickshire
The Hon. Lady Butler
Telephone: 44 (926) 651950

Wiltshire
Lord Seymour, A.R.I.C.S.
Telephone: 44 (98 53) 525

Yorkshire
John Phillips
Henrietta Graham
8-12 Montpellier Parade
Harrogate
North Yorkshire HG1 2TJ
Telephone: 44 (423) 501466/7

Scotland
John Robertson
112 George Street
Edinburgh EH2 4LH
Telephone: 44 (31) 226 7201

Anthony Weld Forester
146 West Regent Street
Glasgow G2 2RQ
Telephone: 44 (41) 221 4817

The Marquis of Huntly
Telephone: Banchory 44 (3302) 4007

Channel Islands
Enquiries to: Robin Townley
Sotheby's Valuations Department
Telephone: 44 (1) 493-8080

Northern Ireland
William Montgomery
The Estate Office, Greyabbey,
Newtownards, Co. Down
Northern Island
Telephone: 353 (24 774) 666

Ireland
William Montgomery
Charles Martin
123a Upper Abbey Street
Dublin 1
Telephone: 353 (1) 734811

Julia Keane
Cappoquin, Co. Waterford
Telephone: 353 (58) 54258

ARGENTINA
Mrs. Mallory Hathaway de Gravière
Avenida Quintana 475
Buenos Aires
Telephone: 54 (1) 8046418

William R. Edbrooke
Kerteux Antiques
Libertad 846, Buenos Aires
Telephone: 54 (1) 393 0831
Attention: Bill Edbrooke

AUSTRALIA

Melbourne
Ann Roberts
606 High Street
East Prahran
Melbourne, Victoria 3181
Telephone: 61 (3) 529 7999
FAX: 61 (3) 525 1346

Sydney
Robert Bleakley
13 Gurner Street,
Paddington
Sydney, New South Wales 2021
Telephone: 61 (2) 332 3500
FAX: 61 (2) 332 2409

AUSTRIA
Dr. Agnes Husslein
Palais Breuner,
Singerstrasse 16, 1010 Vienna
Telephone: 43 (222) 524772/3 or
5133774
Telex: 111868 SKA A

BELGIUM
Count Henry de Limburg Stirum
32 Rue de l'Abbaye,
Brussels 1050
Telephone: 32 (2) 343 50 07
Telex: 61339, SPBBXL B

BRAZIL

Rio de Janeiro
Walter Geyerhahn
Rua do Rosario 155
2° Andar
Rio de Janeiro 20041
Telephone: 55 (21) 222 7771

Helòise Guinlé
Caixa Postal 1199
Rio de Janeiro, RJ CEP2001
Telephone: 55 (21) 552 5769

Sao Paulo
Cornelius O. K. Reichenheim
Alameda Ministro Rocha
Azevedo 391, Sao Paulo 01410
Telephone: 55 (11) 282 1599 &
282 0581

Pedro Correa do Lago
Rua Joao Cachoeira, 267
Sao Paulo 04535
Telephone: 55 (11) 282 3135

DENMARK
Baroness
Hanne Wedell-Wedellsborg
Bredgade 27
1260 Copenhagen K
Telephone: 45 (1) 13 55 56

FRANCE
Count Henry de Limburg Stirum
Alexandre Pradère
Comtesse Anne de Labriffe
(Associate)
Princesse Laure de Beauvau Craon
(Associate)
3 Rue de Miromesnil
75008 Paris
Telephone: 33 (1) 4266 4060
Telex: SPBF A 640084F

GERMANY
Dr. Christoph Graf Douglas
(Managing Director-Germany)
Frankfurt
Telephone: 49 (69) 74 07 87

Cologne
Ursula Niggemann,
St. Apern-Strasse 17-29,
(Kreishaus Galerie)
D-5000 Cologne 1
Telephone: 49 (221) 23 52 84/5
Telex: 8882744 SOTK

Frankfurt
Johannes Ernst
Beethovenstrasse 71
D-6000 Frankfurt/M.1
Telephone: 49 (69) 74 07 87
Telex: 413479

Hamburg
Peter Graf zu Eltz
Ballindamm 17
2000 Hamburg 1
Telephone: 49 (40) 337553
Telex: 2165180 SOTH D

Munich
Heinrich Graf von Spreti
Odeonsplatz 16, D-8000 Munich 22
Telephone: 49 (89) 22 23 75/6
Telex: 523443 ABINIT D

HOLLAND
Jan Pieter Glerum
Malcolm Barber
John Van Schaik
102 Rokin, 1012 KZ Amsterdam
Telephone: 31 (20) 27 5656
Telex: 13267 MAKSO NL

HONG KONG
Suzanne Tory
901-5 Lane Crawford House
70 Queen's Road Central
Hong Kong
Telephone: 852 (5) 248121
Telex: 80163 SPBHX

HUNGRY
Novotrade Inc.
Furst S.u. 24-26
H-1136 Budapest
Telephone: 36 (1) 110687 310546
Telex: 225959 NOVTR H ·

ISRAEL
Rivka Saker
Daniella Luxembourg
Dov Hoz 19
Tel Aviv 63416, Israel
Telephone: 972 (3) 223822
Telex: 361 595 Danet IL
Attn: Sotheby's

ITALY

Florence
Julien Stock
Michael Thomson-Glover
Palazzo Capponi
Via Gino Capponi 26,
50121 Florence
Telephone: 39 (55) 2479021
Telex: 572478 ABINIT I

Milan
Bruno Muheim
Via Pietro Mascagni 15/2
20121 Milan
Telephone: 39 (2) 783911
Telex: 322098 ABINIT I

Rome
Guy de Lotbinière
Piazza di Spagna 90
00186 Rome
Telephone: 39 (6) 678 1798 &
678 2734
Telex: 623282 ABINIT I

Turin
Laura Russo
Corso Galileo Ferraris 18B,
10100 Turin
Telephone: 39 (11) 544898

JAPAN
Miss Kazuko Shiomi
Pisa Counter, Tokyo Prince Hotel,
3-3-1 Shiba-koen,
Minatoku, Tokyo 105
Telephone: 81 (3) 437-1916
Telex: J23255 SEIBPISA

MONACO
Léon Leroy
B.P. 45, Le Sporting d'Hiver,
Place du Casino,
MC 98001, Monaco Cedex
Telephone: 33 (93) 30 88 80
Telex: 479471 SPBMON MC
FAX: 33 (93) 25 24 98

NORWAY
Ingeborg Astrup
Bjornveien 42
0387 Oslo 3
Telephone: 47 (2) 1472 82

PORTUGAL
Frederico Horta e Costa
Casa de S. Miguel
Avenida da Franca
2765 Estoril
Portugal
Telephone: 351 (1) 267 0611

SINGAPORE
Quek Chin Yeow
02-15 Hilton
International Singapore
581 Orchard Road
Singapore 0923
Telephone: (65) 7328239
Telex: RS 34745HPPL

SPAIN
Edmund Peel
Plaza de la Independencia 8
28001-Madrid
Telephone: 34 (1) 522 2902
Telex: 46787 SPBS E

Rocio Tassara
Luis Monreal Tejada (Associate)
Centro de Anticuarios No. 40
Paseo de Gracia 55-57,
08007 Barcelona
Telephone: 34 (3) 215 2008 or
215 2149

SWEDEN AND FINLAND
Hans Dyhlen
Arsenalsgatan 4,
111 47 Stockholm
Telephone: 46 (8) 101478/9
Telex: 17380 SPBSCAN S

SWITZERLAND
Simon de Pury
(Chairman-Switzerland)
Geneva
Telephone: 41 (22) 32 8585

Geneva
Nicholas C. Rayner
13 Quai du Mont Blanc
CH1201 Geneva,
Telephone: 41 (22) 328585
Telex: 429098 SPB CH

Zurich
Ully Wille
20 Bleicherweg, CH-8002 Zurich
Telephone: 41 (1) 202 0011
Telex: 815 333 SOTH CH

TAIWAN R.O.C.
Rita Wong
49 An Ho Road, 4th Floor
Taipei, Taiwan, R.O.C.
Telephone: 886 (2) 776 1991
Telex: 24429 ANDARI

SOTHEBY'S

FOUNDED 1744

Absentee Bid Form

Sotheby's 1334 York Avenue, New York, N.Y. 10021
Bid Department (212) 606-7414
Important: Please see "Guide for Absentee Bidders" on the reverse of this sheet.

Sale Title	**Date**	**Sale Code**
The Linda and Gerald Guterman Collection	January 14, 1988	"GUTERMAN" 5676

I wish to place the following bids for this sale to be held on January 14, 1988. These bids are to be executed by Sotheby's up to but not exceeding the amount or amounts specified below. Each bid is PER LOT, as indicated, and all bids will be executed and are accepted subject to the "Conditions of Sale" and "Terms of Guarantee" printed in the catalogue of this sale. Please note that a premium of 10% will be added to the hammer price as part of the total purchase price.

Arranging Payment

In order to avoid delays in receiving purchases, buyers unknown to us are advised to make payment arrangements or supply credit references in advance of the sale date. If such arrangements are not made, purchases cannot leave our premises until checks have been cleared.

Name (please print or type)

Date

Address

City, State   Zip Code   Telephone

☐ Please check if this is a new address.

Please Mail to:

Sotheby's Bid Department
1334 York Avenue
New York, N.Y. 10021

Bank reference or deposit (If bidder is unknown to Sotheby's)

Signed   Resale Number (If applicable)

Lot Number	Item	Top Limit of Bid not including 10% premium (Bid is per lot number as listed in the catalogue
		$
		$
		$
		$
		$
		$
		$
		$
		$
		$
		$
		$

9/85 BS

Guide for Absentee Bidders

Absentee Bids

If you are unable to attend an auction in person, and wish to place bids, you may give Sotheby's Bid Department instructions to bid on your behalf. Our representatives will then try to purchase the lot or lots of your choice for the lowest price possible, and never for more than the top amount you indicate. This service is free and confidential. Please note: Sotheby's offers this service as a convenience to clients who are unable to attend the sale, and although we will make every effort, Sotheby's will not be responsible for error or failure to execute bids.

Placing Absentee Bids

To place bids, please use the absentee bid form provided in this catalogue. Be sure to accurately record the lot numbers and descriptions and the top price you are willing to pay for each lot. "Buy" or unlimited bids will not be accepted. Always indicate a "top limit" – the amount to which you would bid if you were attending the auction yourself.

Alternative bids should be indicated by using the word "OR" between lot numbers. Then if your bid on an early lot is successful, we will not continue to bid on other lots for you. Or, if your early bids are unsuccessful, we will continue to execute bids for alternative lots until a bid is successful. Bids must always be placed in the same order as the lot numbers appear in the catalogue.

Each absentee bid form should contain bids for one sale only; the number and code name should appear in the top right hand corner of the form. Please place your bids as early as possible. In the event of identical bids, the earliest received will take precedence.

Telephone Bids

Bids may be placed by telephone, but are accepted only at Sotheby's discretion and at the caller's risk. Telephone bids should always be confirmed by letter or telegram.

Buyer's Premium

The "top limit" you indicate on your bid form is for the hammer price exclusively. Please keep in mind that a premium of 10% will be added to the hammer price of each lot you buy and is payable by you together with the applicable sales tax which is applied to the total cost of your purchase. (The total cost includes the buyer's premium).

Successful Bids

Successful bidders will be notified and invoiced within a few days of the sale. All bidders will receive a list of sale results if they purchased the sale catalogue or enclose a stamped self-addressed envelope with their absentee bid form.

For More Information

To place telephone bids, or for further information, please call Roberta Louckx at (212) 606-7414, or the regional office in your area.

Guide for Shipment of Purchases

Shipping/Forwarding Instructions

If your bid is successful, we can arrange to have your property shipped to you. As shipping costs can be expensive, we suggest that you request a quotation from our Art Transport Department at (212) 606-7511. If an estimate of shipping costs is not requested prior to shipment, we will act according to the instructions you provide. All shipments will be C.O.D.

The packing and shipping of items by Sotheby's employees is undertaken solely at our discretion. Furniture, larger items and high-valued property may require the services of professional packers.

Upon receipt of payment, Sotheby's will instruct packers and carriers. Your attention is drawn to the Conditions of Sale which require payment and clearance promptly after the sale. In default of these conditions, lots may be transferred to a public warehouse at the risk and expense of the purchaser. As stated in the Conditions of Sale, we are not responsible for the acts or omissions of carriers or packers, whether or not recommended by us. Packing and handling of purchased lots by us is at the entire risk of the purchaser.

Please allow 4–6 weeks for delivery.

Methods of Transport

Air Freight – Not to be confused with air mail, this method employs air freight carriers to ship property that has already been packed.

Registered Parcel Post – Parcels which do not exceed the size and weight limits set by the United States Postal Service may be sent by this method. In the case of international shipments, it is not always possible to insure parcels for their full value. Please consult the Art Transport Department for details.

Truck – This method is recommended for large shipments and the transport of any item of furniture. There are also "shuttle services" which can transport uncrated paintings and works of art to specific areas in the United States. The Art Transport Department can supply complete details.

Book Post – This is a less expensive, but slower, method of shipping books via the United Postal Service. Parcels shipped in this manner can be insured only for a maximum of $400.

For More Information

To receive an estimate of shipping costs, or for further information, please call Laura Bowman at (212) 606-7511, or the regional office in your area.

Cover design:
Barbara Olejniczak

Color separations:
Toppan Printing Company

Consultant Art Director:
Alan Hartwell, New York

Printed and Typeset in the U.S.A. by Village Craftsmen, Inc. Rosemont, New Jersey